FARTHER
The Quest for Distance

TERRY GWYNN-JONES

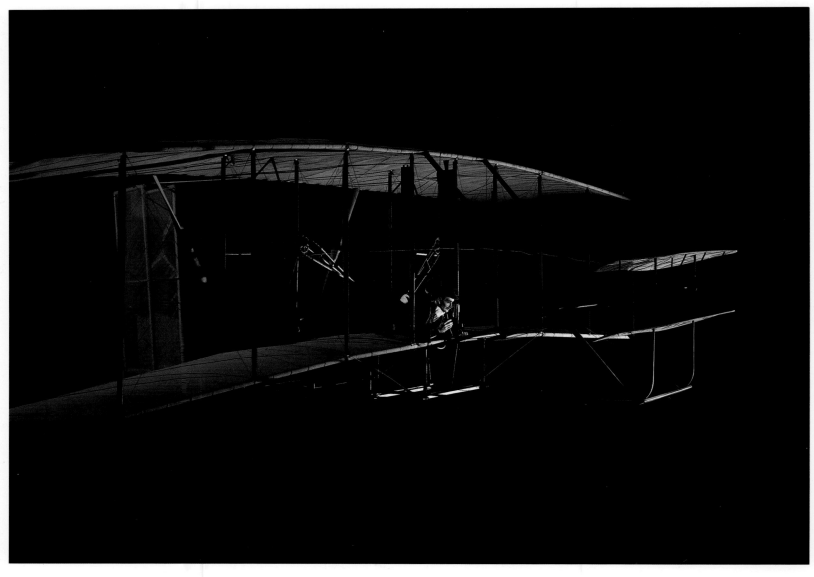

The Wright *Flyer* occupies the central position of honor in the Main Gallery of the Smithsonian Institution's National Air and Space Museum.

The Vickers Vimy was produced late in World War I as a heavy bomber. Although originally designed to lift 5,400 pounds of fuel and bombs, this special trans-Atlantic Vimy carried 8,650 pounds of fuel as Alcock and Brown staggered off Lester's Field, Newfoundland. Struggling for height, it briefly disappeared behind the low tree-covered rise shown in this photograph. Onlookers thought the Vimy had crashed.

The first nonstop trans-Atlantic flight ended with the crippled Vickers Vimy perched tail-up in an Irish bog. Soldiers from a nearby military installation thought Alcock and Brown were joking when they claimed to have flown the Atlantic. When a local asked about the crash landing, Alcock replied: "Your bog is like the Irish question, not as easy as it looks. . . ."

our instinct of balance. The machine, left to its own devices, swung, flew amok, and began to perform circus tricks," Brown recalled. A violent spin took them to within a few hundred feet of the sea before they broke through the clouds in a nearly vertical turn. Later in the flight, ice threatened to stop one engine and for a time jammed the ailerons.

When they finally crossed the cloud-shrouded coast of Ireland, Alcock decided to play it safe and land on what appeared to be a lush green meadow. The 16½-hour flight ended minutes later with the Vimy ingloriously perched tail up and nose down in an Irish peat bog. It mattered little. They had crossed the ocean nonstop and were heroes. The pair received congratulations from President Woodrow Wilson and knighthoods from King George V. Canadian headlines dubbed the men "Lords of the Air," and the British press wrote of their "imperishable record." American journalists were equally generous in their praise.

"Like Alexander, the record-making aviator will soon weep because he has no more worlds to conquer. . . . For human daring our hats are off to these Englishmen who fought the sun, the stars and Sir Isaac Newton's best theory and beat them all," the New York *Times* editorialized. Handing them the $50,000 winner's check, the then Secretary of State for War, Winston

Britain's triumphant trans-Atlantic airmen, Sir John Alcock (left) and Sir Arthur Whitten-Brown, photographed by a Vickers Vimy shortly after their flight in 1919. Generously giving the credit to his navigator, Alcock told newsmen: "My part was simple. It's my trade. The navigation was the ticklish part." Six months later Alcock died, crashing in fog while delivering a Vickers Viking amphibian to France.

Churchill, quipped, "I don't really know what we should admire most in our guests: their audacity, their determination, their skill . . . or their good fortune."

Audacious, determined, skilled they were indeed, as had been all the fliers involved in the Atlantic challenge. None would have denied that both the British and American crews had also had their fair share of luck. Nevertheless, the Atlantic victory had confirmed Vickers's faith in the reliability of their Vimy, particularly its 360-horsepower Rolls-Royce Eagle VIII engines. With plans to market a civil version of the bomber, the company entered a sister ship in the second great long-distance contest of 1919—a flight between England and Australia.

On to Australia

Australia's irascible prime minister, Billy Hughes, promoted the marathon flight. The Welsh-born politician had made several passenger flights and was conscious of the role airplanes might play in his sparsely settled and isolated homeland.

"With a view to stimulating aerial activity, the Commonwealth Government has decided to offer £10,000 for the first successful flight to Australia from Great Britain, in a machine manned by Australians," the official announcement proclaimed. The rules stipulated that the flight had to be completed in 30 days.

Equally conscious of the need to arouse interest in commercial flying, Britain's Controller of Civil Aviation, Major General Sir F. H. Sykes, applauded, saying: "I hope all the other Dominions will follow. Then we shall be able to have great prizes hanging out as bait to all ends of the world." However, some Australian newspapers were critical of the government's scheme. The Melbourne *Age* described it as "A circus flight—a poorly disguised attempt at self-advertisement at the expense of the Australian public."

Though lacking the Atlantic's over-water drama, the 11,340-mile England-to-Australia flight represented a much greater test of endurance for both men and machines. Crews faced the hazards of the European winter, the torrid heat and dust of the Middle East, and severe tropical storms. Of great significance was the fact that the flight was virtually pioneering Europe's future air routes to India, Singapore, the Dutch East Indies, and Australia.

The Vimy was the favorite. The Australian Flying Corps pilots and brothers Captain Ross Smith and Lieutenant Keith Smith were the pilots. Ross Smith's former wartime mechanics, Sergeants Wally Shiers and Jim Bennett, completed the tightly knit crew. Besides the Vimy's Atlantic performance, a major factor in their favor was Ross Smith's wartime experience in desert operations; he had been personal pilot to Lawrence of Arabia. Furthermore, he had already flown the desert route from Cairo to Calcutta.

By early December, four aircraft were spread along the route; a fifth had crashed minutes after takeoff, killing its two crewmen. Across Europe, sleet and snowstorms had slowed all the competitors. On board the Vimy G-EAOU, which the crew joked stood for "God 'Elp All of Us," the windshield iced over and the Smith brothers took turns peering ahead. Each could watch for only a few minutes before their goggles clogged with snow and their faces were covered with icy masks. Even their sandwiches froze solid. In his log, Ross Smith wrote: "This sort of flying is rotten. The cold is hell. I am a silly ass for ever embarking on such a flight."

The crew of a second aircraft was killed when they crashed at night off the coast of Greece. After flying a circuitous route through central Europe to bypass bad weather, another crew was forced down in Yugoslavia and arrested as Bolshevik spies. The remaining contender, the future polar explorer Captain (Sir) Hubert Wilkins, flying a twin-engine Blackburn Kangaroo bomber, force-landed in Crete after an engine failure.

The Vimy kept going. In Egypt, Shiers saved an overheating engine by using chewing gum and friction tape to repair a cracked induction manifold. Resting in the desert near Baghdad, the airmen were caught in a violent sandstorm and, assisted by 50 Bengal Lancers, spent the night holding down the flailing Vimy.

Across Burma and Thailand, down the Malay peninsula to Singapore,

The crew of the Vickers Vimy G-EAOU—with grim humor the airmen said it stood for "God 'elp All Of Us"—stop for a refreshment break in the Australian outback.

violent storms threatened and thrashed the flyers. At Surabaya, bogged in mud, they got away after villagers helped them construct a "runway" of laced bamboo matting: a similar principle employing steel mesh would be used during World War II.

On December 10, days out from London, the Vimy made the 466-mile crossing of the shark-infested Timor Sea and landed at Darwin in northern Australia. They had completed the epic journey in 135 hours of flight time, averaging 75 mph. Australia went aviation-mad. The Smith brothers received knighthoods, and newspapers talked of air services to Europe. Although an international service was still years away, Billy Hughes's grand gesture had paid off by awakening Australians to the possibility of air travel. The following year, Norman Brearley's pioneering West Australian Airways commenced operations; shortly afterward, Queensland and Northern Territory Aerial Service (QANTAS) flew its first outback airline service.

The 1919 successes of the Vimy led to the development of a modified 10-passenger version named the Commercial. Only a few were sold, but they were first in a long line of Vickers airliners. The risks and costs also paid off for Rolls-Royce, which had manufactured the engines for all the British Atlantic challengers and four of the five entrants in the flight to Australia. Their remarkable 360-horsepower Eagle engines earned for the company a reputation for performance and reliability that was to carry them into the future.

Despite the excitement of 1919, the outlook for commercial aviation remained bleak. Worldwide, about a dozen companies were attempting to run profitable airline operations. Likening the problems that faced aviation to those of the early railway engineers, Britain's *Flight* magazine suggested: "It was a very long time before the thinking and conservative public could be brought to discard travel by stage coach and trust themselves to be hustled through the country behind a locomotive. In the matter of aviation there are two things which have to be done. The first is to try out design and construction. The second is to create and maintain public interest and confidence in the aeroplane as a means of travel."

In Great Britain, the short-sighted government did not help the cause, refusing to subsidize commercial aviation. However, in mainland Europe, where the devastation of war had seriously disrupted surface transport in France and Belgium, operators received generous encouragement. In

At Darwin's specially constructed Fanny Bay Airfield, the frontier townsfolk gathered to greet the airmen. Sir Hudson Fysh, who later founded Qantas, recalled the touchdown: "It was one of the most moving sights I can remember. The termination of one of the greatest flights, if not the greatest, in the history of aviation."

Germany and Holland, this support stimulated the design of a new generation of monoplane airliners that would put them years ahead of other nations. In the United States, both civil and military aviation faced an even greater task gaining acceptance.

The leading edge of heavy aircraft design in 1917, the Vickers Vimy G-EAOU is preserved in a special building at Adelaide Airport, South Australia.

Early Postwar Aviation in the United States

Unlike Europe, the United States did not have available for commercial use a glut of unwanted large military combat aircraft, but plenty of surplus de Havilland DH-4s and DH-9s were available to satisfy the Air Service's needs for years to come. Moreover, the war had not seriously disrupted surface transport. A superb railway service linked most towns and cities, and with aircraft of the day uncomfortable and hard-pressed to average 80 mph, they offered no real advantage over the speed, luxury, and safety of Pullman trains. Moreover, the United States lacked a significant international catalyst, unlike Great Britain and many other European nations, which saw the airplane as a possible future link with far-flung empires. Consequently, the American airlines remained years away.

The struggling U.S. Air Mail Service relied mainly on its Liberty engine powered war-surplus de Havilland DH-4s. In 1920, its airmen flew the first transcontinental airmail. Taking off from Hazelhurst Field, New York, on September 8, an aging DH-4 carried 16,000 letters—some in a suitcase strapped to the wing—on the first leg to Iowa City. Three days later, following a Pony Express—like relay of pilots and planes, the mail reached San Francisco.

For most American surplus military pilots, a career in commercial aviation started with the hand-to-mouth life of an itinerant barnstormer, often in a surplus Curtiss JN-4 Jenny. A handful found work with the struggling air mail service, which, started by the United States Post Office in 1918, had flown 18,806 hours and carried 49 million letters by the end of 1920. In February 1921, as some members of Congress were calling for its disbanding, mail pilots had reduced the coast-to-coast time to 26 hours, prompting the New York *Tribune* to comment: "The feat completed Wednesday was by the very service which certain elements in Congress have just fought desperately to destroy. Can antagonism be continued against such a service with such a record?"

The air mail service was not alone in its battle for survival. With the war over, the government was not interested in the future of military and naval aviation, and appropriations were cut to the bone. There was barely enough to cover the payroll and fuel bills, let alone replace the war-weary de Havilland DH-4s and Curtiss Jenny trainers. This situation had prompted the Navy's trans-Atlantic flight of May 1919.

The plight of U.S. Army aviation was of particular concern to its chief after 1921, Major General Mason M. Patrick. Working behind the scenes, Patrick allowed his outspoken assistant, Brigadier General William "Billy" Mitchell, to be the belligerent advocate of air power, leading the fight for more funds and new aircraft. To demonstrate the versatility of the airplane and keep the service in the public eye, Mitchell encouraged Army pilots to embark on a series of long-distance flights.

The first, a coast-to-coast reliability trial in 1919, had backfired when nine pilots lost their lives. "It proved the necessity of weather reports and other meteorological information for pilots on cross-country flights," the Aircraft Manufacturers Association, Inc., had reported in its 1920 *Aircraft Year Book*. Subsequent Army flights were extremely successful: around the nation's borders; New York to Nome, Alaska; and a series of transcontinental dashes. These flights highlighted the reliability of the Liberty engine that was to be the mainstay of American aviation in the early 1920s. Indeed, it was the Liberty's reliability that in 1923 enabled the Army to achieve the headlines Mitchell had sought.

Given a small appropriation to evaluate new aircraft, Mitchell had purchased two of Anthony Fokker's F. IV high-wing transports, which were modified to take a Liberty 12 engine. The Dutch designer's single-engine monoplanes, along with Hugo Junkers's low-wing F13, were already in airline service in Europe and were swinging the pendulum away from biplanes toward more aerodynamically efficient monoplanes.

The Army Air Service's Fokker F. IVs, called T-2s, were powered by the 400-horsepower Packard Liberty engine, carried eight passengers, and could fly six hours on 130 gallons of fuel. During engineering trials at McCook Field, Ohio, test pilots Lieutenants Oakland G. Kelly and Muir S. Fairchild, who had already begun studying potential aircraft for a nonstop transcontinental flight, determined that a modified T-2 had the load-carrying capacity for such an undertaking. Patrick and Mitchell approved the project in August

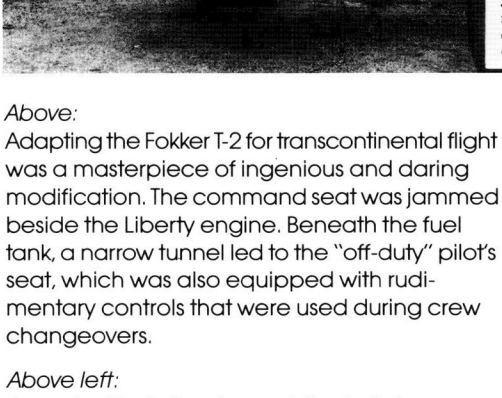

Above:
Adapting the Fokker T-2 for transcontinental flight was a masterpiece of ingenious and daring modification. The command seat was jammed beside the Liberty engine. Beneath the fuel tank, a narrow tunnel led to the "off-duty" pilot's seat, which was also equipped with rudimentary controls that were used during crew changeovers.

Above left:
An ardent but abrasive architect of air power, Brigadier General William "Billy" Mitchell (left) got a new boss after his famous 1921 bombing demonstration that upset the Navy. The new Army Air Service Chief, Major General Mason M. Patrick (right), became an equally determined though more tactful supporter of the Air Service and encouraged the Army's pioneering long-distance flights. General Patrick believed strongly that he had to be a flyer himself to understand aviation and establish credibility with his aviators, and so he learned to fly and earned his military aviator's wings in 1923 at the age of 59.

Left:
The Junkers F 13, which first flew in June 1919, was the first all-metal, low-wing monoplane with an enclosed cabin to enter civil airline service. It served in many airlines throughout the world and had an excellent record. The F 13 featured Hugo Junkers's use of duralumin for the airframe and the corrugated metal skin that became a standard feature of Junkers aircraft into the 1930s.

Lieutenants John Macready (left) and Oakley Kelly display their Fokker T-2's transcontinental load of 737 gallons of gasoline and 40 gallons of oil. Calculating that with an 11,000-pound takeoff weight the Fokker's theoretical absolute ceiling would be an inch above ground level, they took off at 10,850 pounds.

The route followed by Kelly and Macready on the first nonstop coast-to-coast flight. Proud of their navigation, Macready wrote: "We drew a line across the continent on the map and followed it at night and during the day, with our compass the main reliance a large part of the time. We followed no railroad or established air or mail route and kept our course and exact location throughout, except when high elevations forced us to temporarily deflect from this line."

1922. Lieutenant John A. Macready, McCook's chief test pilot, was soon appointed copilot when Fairchild was injured in an accident.

The flight was planned with the minute attention to detail that would become the hallmark of NASA's astronaut expeditions a half century later. Besides strengthening the wings and adding extra fuel and oil tanks, they tested various fuels and oils to guarantee the best performance. There was room for only one pilot at the control seat, which was jammed alongside the roaring Liberty engine. An "off-duty" crew position equipped with auxiliary controls was built in the rear of the cabin behind a 450-gallon auxiliary fuel tank. After studying the terrain and weather patterns, the flyers chose a west—east route, starting from Rockwell Field in San Diego, California, and ending at Roosevelt Field on Long Island.

Following two abortive attempts in October and November 1922, one

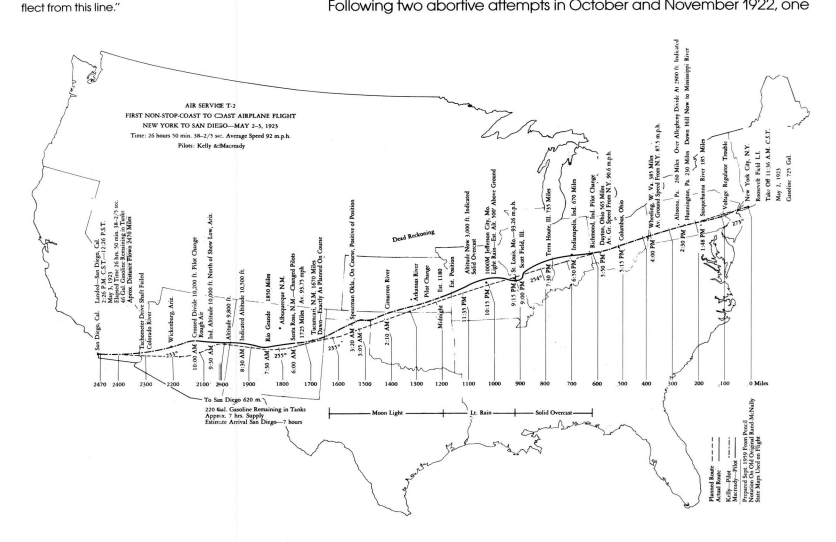

stopped by clouds over the California coastal ranges and the other thwarted by a leaking radiator and cracked cylinder jacket over Indiana, the airmen set off again on May 2, 1923, this time heading west from Roosevelt Field. They needed a push from the ground crew to start the takeoff roll and even then only just got airborne. For the first 20 minutes Kelly flew in ground effect, barely clearing telegraph poles and power lines, waiting for fuel burn-off to reduce the weight. Macready later described their harrowing start: "We scraped along the housetops and hillsides with our Liberty motor running absolutely full power, and for hours we felt as though we could stick out our hands and grab a handful of daisies off the fields."

After they eventually crawled to 1,000 feet and repaired the generator in flight—one advantage of sharing the cabin with the engine—the remainder of the flight was almost an anti-climax of precise, routine operation. Navigation was accomplished by the method of the time: map reading by day and pinpointing the lights of the towns and cities at night. The only surface aid to navigation was a lone searchlight beamed up over Illinois. Exhausted but elated, Kelly and Macready reached San Diego in 26 hours and 50 minutes, averaging 92 mph over 2,470 miles.

"The greatest significance of this flight is that aviation, given half a chance, will be the greatest factor for progress that has ever existed in the history of civilization," *U.S. Air Service* magazine commented pointedly. A more telling comment came in a fan telegram from 93-year-old Ezra Meeker of New York that read: "Congratulations on your wonderful flight, which beats my time made 71 years ago by ox team at two miles an hour, five months on the way. . . . Ready to go with you next time."

Given reliable engines, the limited fuel-carrying capacity of the aircraft and the endurance of the crew were the primary restrictions on long-distance flying. Even the standard twin-engine bombers of the early 1920s had ranges of only 500 to 600 miles, and so repeated landings and refuelings were necessary to achieve greater distance. If the aircraft could be refueled in flight, only the crew's endurance and mechanical failure would limit the range. Lieutenants Lowell Smith and John Richter completed the first in-flight refueling over Rockwell Field on June 27, 1923. Then, on August 27 and 28, they flew for 37 hours and 15 minutes (3,291 miles) and were refueled 15 times. The great potential of this technique for extending an aircraft's range was shown in January 1929 when an Air Corps Fokker C-2A, the *Question Mark*, established an air refueling endurance record of 150 hours over

The transcontinental flight of the much modified Fokker T-2 was conducted to promote the U.S. Army Air Service. It generated public uproar when it was announced that as junior officers, Lieutenants Kelly and Macready were barred by red tape from receiving promotion. "The President is only empowered to confer promotions on those officers with ratings of colonel and higher," Secretary of War Weeks told a *Los Angeles Times* reporter, adding lamely, "I will write them a nice letter." The military eventually awarded both men the Distinguished Flying Cross.

AERIAL REFUELING

From the beginning of powered flight, designers and aviators have sought ways to fly farther without stopping to refuel. One obvious solution was larger aircraft that could carry the greater quantities of aviation gasoline required for long-distance flights. Another was more efficient engines that used less fuel. A third was for one aircraft to refuel another in flight so that stopping would be unnecessary until the destination had been reached, the crew was exhausted, or a mechanical failure occurred.

The U.S. Army Air Service took the lead in experimenting with in-flight refueling techniques in the 1920s. Lieutenants Lowell Smith, who later led the around-the-world flight of 1924, and John Richter modified a DH-4B with additional fuel tanks and a hose that could be lowered to transfer fuel to a second modified DH-4B while in flight. They first demonstrated this technique over Rockwell Field, San Diego, California, on June 27, 1923. On August 27 and 28, they flew the DH-4B over San Diego for 37 hours and 16 minutes, with 15 refuelings by the tanker aircraft.

Several years later, the Belgians Crooy and Groenen extended refueled time in the air to 60 hours and 7 minutes. The U.S. Army Air Corps set a world mark in early January 1929 when a Fokker C-2A transport, the *Question Mark*, flew for 150 hours over southern California without landing. The crew, which included future Air Force leaders Carl A. "Tooey" Spaatz, Ira C. Eaker, and Elwood "Pete" Quesada, flew nearly 13,500 miles, and the aircraft was refueled 37 times, receiving 5,600 gallons of gasoline and 245 gallons of oil. In-flight refueling had obvious military implications, as Spaatz reported, because bombers could take off with lighter fuel loads and thus more bombs, be refueled, and have an almost unlimited radius of action.

In September 1934, Alan Cobham outfitted his Airspeed Courier to fly nonstop from London to India, refueled in flight by a Handley Page W.10 aerial tanker. Cobham reached Malta before mechanical difficulties forced him to land. He later formed Flight Refueling, Ltd., that did additional work on aerial refueling techniques and equipment, but the pressures and realities of World War II did little to stimulate further development.

In the early postwar years, the British pushed the "probe-and-drogue," or trailing hose, method of in-flight refueling. Faced with significant range problems in reaching potential Soviet targets with its B-29s, the U.S. Air Force turned to aerial refueling as a way to increase the combat range of its aircraft while awaiting the intercontinental B-36s and B-52s that were in production and development. In November 1947, the Air Force asked Boeing to convert a B-29 to a tanker configuration using the British probe-and-drogue gravity feed system. Experiments with the new KB-29 in May 1948 proved the concept, and the Air Force directed Boeing to convert more B-29s to KB-29 aerial tankers. The KB-29s that refueled the B-50A *Lucky Lady II* on its 94-hour around-the-world flight from February 26 to March 2, 1949, conclusively proved the ability of in-flight refueling to extend the combat radius of the Strategic Air Command's bomber force. With tankers at forward air bases, SAC's medium bombers—B-29s, B-50s, and the new all-jet B-47s—could be based securely in the continental United States and strike any target in the world within hours.

As was typical of Boeing, when the Air Force first directed the new tanker program, the company developed some of its own concepts into important realities. In May 1948, Boeing suggested a new type of refueling apparatus, a "flying boom," to replace the probe-and-drogue system. The Boeing concept was a rigid system of telescoping pipes and pumps that could provide more fuel per minute to the receiver. Fitted to a KB-29, the Boeing system was so successful that the Air Force soon began converting its B-50s to KB-50K tankers with the flying boom system.

Conversion of aging bombers was not the solution to the worldwide refueling requirements of the Air Force, especially with the all-jet B-47s replacing the older piston-engine B-29s and B-50s. In 1950, Boeing and the Air Force converted a C-97A Stratofreighter—the military equivalent of the commercial Model 377 Stratocruiser—to an aerial tanker as the KC-97. By 1953 Boeing had produced 801 KC-97E/F/Gs for the Air Force, primarily to refuel the B-47s.

1944: A MONUMENTAL JAPANESE FLIGHT

One of the most remarkable long-distance flights was completed by a Japanese aircraft during World War II. Its genesis went back to Charles Lindbergh's 1927 conquest of the Atlantic.

Determined to establish its aviation credentials, Japan searched for its own Lindbergh to make the first nonstop Pacific crossing. After an abortive plan involving an overgrown Kawanishi-built copy of Lindbergh's Ryan, two Japanese attempts employing Junkers A-50s failed. The flight became a national obsession. Even after the American *Miss Veedol* completed the crossing in 1931, Japanese airmen made another valiant attempt that ended when their Junkers W.33 vanished.

In 1940, Japan's *Asahi Shimbun* newspaper, which had promoted numerous long-distance flights, proposed a nonstop goodwill flight from Tokyo to New York. Two special twin-engine Tachikawa A-26 (Ki-77) aircraft designed to fly more than 11,185 miles were constructed. Powered by 1,170-horsepower Nakajima Ha-115 radials, the A-26 weighed nearly 37,000 pounds carrying its maximum 3,052-gallon fuel load. However, because of its 96-foot-span high-aspect-ratio wing, the monoplane needed only a 4,500-foot takeoff run.

The flight was scheduled for 1942, but Japan's entry into World War II in December 1941 aborted the project. One Ki-77 was lost on a clandestine flight from Singapore to Berlin in July 1943. In July 1944, to prove that the Ki-77 could have reached New York, the second aircraft circled over Manchuria for an unofficial record of 10,212 miles in 57 hours and 12 minutes. It was the equivalent of flying from Tokyo to New York with nearly 3,500 miles to spare! Had the war not intervened, Japan's long-legged Tachikawa might have preempted by 34 years the achievement eventually accomplished by a Boeing 747SP in 1975.

This naive design exercise prompted Japan to develop its own long-distance machine, the Tachikawa A-26 (Ki-77), which eventually set an astonishing distance record during World War II.

In October 1927, attention turned to the south Atlantic, where France's Dieudonné Costes prepared for a nonstop crossing. Since Portugal's dramatic 1923 marathon, Spain's Ramon Franco and Italy's Marchese de Pinedo, both utilizing Dornier Wal flying boats, had also made staged crossings. Mussolini had ordered the Italian effort "for the glory of Fascist Italy."

Costes and his navigator, Joseph Le Brix, planned to restore lost national pride after the crash of *L'Oiseau Blanc*. Honoring their dead comrades, they named their Breguet XIX *Nungesser-Coli*. Their flight from Saint Louis on the Senegalese coast of Africa to Port Natal, Brazil, took 21¼ hours and was followed by a triumphant aerial tour of the United States that ended in San Francisco. Shipping their airplane to Tokyo, they flew home across Asia, arriving back in Paris as France's new aviation heroes. On September 27 to 29, 1929, accompanied by Maurice Bellonte, Costes flew the scarlet Breguet XIX *Point d'Interrogation* (Question Mark) nonstop from Paris to Manchuria—a

France's Dieudonné Costes and his navigator, Joseph Le Brix, made this first nonstop crossing of the south Atlantic on October 14 and 15, 1927. After the crossing, they toured South and North America. Part of the route is emblazoned on the fuselage of their Breguet XIX *Nungesser-Coli*. It was named after two dead comrades who vanished while trying to beat Lindbergh across the north Atlantic in their biplane *L'Oiseau-Blanc*.

Costes and Le Brix over the Canal Zone after their south Atlantic flight. Costes had been chasing records since 1925, when he crashed in Germany trying for a world long-distance record. A year later he finally set a new nonstop mark with a 3,313-mile nonstop flight from Paris to Jask, Iran.

staggering 4,912 miles—and set a new distance record. The following year, the pair achieved France's ultimate aviation goal: a Paris–New York flight.

On April 12 and 13, 1928, Hermann Koehl, James Fitzmaurice, and Baron von Hünefeld in the German Junkers W33 floatplane *Bremen* completed a troubled east–west Atlantic crossing from Ireland, missing New York by 1,000 miles and landing at Greenly Island, Labrador, Canada. The Frenchmen were determined to do better. Setting out from Paris on September 1, 1930, they battled the prevailing winds to New York. When *Point d'Interrogation* arrived 37 hours and 18 minutes later, the scene was reminiscent of Lindbergh's Paris landing. Some 140 policemen held back the crowd as Lindbergh rushed to greet France's greatest long-distance flyers.

Solo to Australia

The public euphoria generated by Lindbergh and Costes during 1927 continued throughout 1928 as Australian and American aviators grabbed world attention. Bert Hinkler fired Australia's opening shot in February 1928 with the first solo England-Australia flight. Unlike Alan Cobham, Hinkler was not concerned with airline pioneering. His interest lay in promoting the light airplane as an economical family tourer of the future. As early as 1920 he had flown nonstop from London to Turin in a tiny Avro Baby. "Let the Zeniths get hold of that," the exhilarated Australian had exclaimed after averaging 32 miles per gallon.

His 1928 dash to Australia was done in Avro's latest sporting biplane, a two-seat Avian powered by a miserly 85-horsepower Cirrus engine. Departing in secret on February 7, he reached India before the press caught up with the news. From then on the world followed his race for home, swept up by the concept of a lone flyer challenging the elements. Flying by day and

Facing page (top left):
The jubilant Costes and Bellonte received a traditional New York ticker-tape parade. The overwhelming reception echoed the emotional greeting France had given Lindbergh three years earlier.

Facing page (top right):
Dieudonné Costes (front cockpit) and Maurice Bellonte prepare for takeoff for New York from Le Bourget airfield, Paris. The weather was not ideal. Costes recalled: "We took off in the face of the mists. Sixty square metres of cloth fabric had to lift 6,300 kilos. Our battle with the elements had begun." The next morning, while her husband was still battling Atlantic storms, Madame Costes told waiting newsmen: "I went to bed last night to dream of him in the great loneliness of the black night over the sea. But how could I sleep?"

Facing page (bottom):
In September 1929, 37 hours after leaving Paris, the scarlet Breguet XIX *Point d'Interrogation* (Question Mark) touched down at New York's Curtiss Field. France's Costes and Bellonte had become the first to link the two cities by flying from east to west against the prevailing wind. Several years earlier globe-trotting French pilots in their long-legged Breguets had started the world craze for nonstop long-distance flying.

Left:
After Bert Hinkler's 1928 solo dash from England to Australia, the folding wings of his Avro Avian enabled it to be towed through the streets of Brisbane. Before his safe arrival, the Australian authorities remained strangely aloof. Wishing to discourage do-or-die flyers who were harming aviation's image, the prime minister had announced that his government would not assist inadequately organized "unofficial" flights.

At the end of his 1928 flight from England, Hinkler toured Australia in his Avro Avian, posing for photographers in the business suit that was his trademark. His modest manner appealed to the average Australian, but he lacked the flair to attract big business backers. Hinkler died in 1933 attempting to set a new England-Australia record.

Hinkler's Avro Avian prototype G-EBOV is displayed in Brisbane's Queensland Museum. Though never achieving the popularity of the de Havilland Moth, Avians made several long-distance record flights from England to Australia and South Africa. In 1930, Sir Charles Kingsford-Smith used his Avian IVA *Southern Cross Junior* to lower Hinkler's England-to-Australia record by nearly six days.

fussing over his engine by night, Hinkler navigated halfway around the world by a *Times* atlas. His 11,005-mile flight took 128 flying hours spread over 15 days, halving the Smith brothers' record that had been set in 1919.

A British newspaper coined the phrase "Hustling Hinkler," and an American composer picked up the theme. Before Hinkler reached home, Tin Pan Alley sheet music pianists were playing "Hustling Hinkler up in the Sky." Australians sported "Hinkler Homburgs" (his favorite headgear), and couples danced the "Hinkler Quickstep." The press called him "the Australian Lindbergh," a title repeated often between October 27 and December 7, 1931, when Hinkler again made world headlines with the first solo flight of a light aircraft from New York to London via the Caribbean, Brazil, western Africa, and Spain.

The Pacific Challenge

The Pacific remained as the last great transoceanic challenge. In June 1927, the U.S. Army galvanized attention with the first flight from the mainland to Hawaii. Having established a chain of Pacific bases stretching to the Philippines, the military wanted to demonstrate the feasibility of flying at least to Hawaii. A Navy effort in 1925 had failed, but that did not deter Army Lieutenants Lester Maitland and Albert Hegenberger from attempting the 2,360-mile flight from Oakland, California.

The Army had recently purchased a Fokker C-2 transport, an American-built version of the F. VIIA/3m trimotor powered by 220-horsepower Wright Whirlwind J-5s. Maitland knew that it could lift the required fuel load. The Army made sure it was fitted with a specially built 71-foot wing and equipped with the latest in blind-flying instruments and navigational and radio equipment. Hegenberger had spent years testing blind-flying instruments and navigation systems and studying the problems of transoceanic operations. He was acutely aware that a small (as little as 3½ degrees) track error could result in their completely missing the tiny island target. Thus he realized the value of the revolutionary new radio navigation system they were to test en route, flying along beams transmitted from radio beacons installed at San Francisco and Hawaii.

The Army Fokker, exotically named *Bird of Paradise*, set off on June 28, 1927. Thirty minutes out, Hegenberger tuned the radio to receive coded signals that indicated whether they were on the beam. The signal kept them on course for about an hour and then stopped because of a receiver problem. From then on, with much of the flight in darkness and cloud, they were forced to rely on Hegenberger's superb dead-reckoning navigation while Maitland flew "blind" on instruments. They reached Wheeler Field, north of Honolulu, safely after 25 hours and 49 minutes.

Hegenberger's prophetic report recommended the establishment of a school of navigation and the provision of more accurate flight instruments. It was a blueprint for American military aviation to move from fair-weather flying to all-weather operations. He wrote: "Without the ability to fly to a distant objective, under adverse conditions if necessary, the vision and striking power means very little. Mobility involves both distance and direction. Under service conditions this means navigation independent of landmarks."

Using superb planning and preparation, the Army airmen had completed the longest nonstop over-water flight to date and proved that Hawaii was a stepping-stone for an island-hopping trans-Pacific flight. Only weeks later, Australian airmen Charles Kingsford-Smith and Charles Ulm arrived in California intent on using the same stepping-stone to bridge aviation's last ocean barrier.

The Australians planned the flight as a prelude to a trans-Pacific air mail service. However, they had trouble finding backers when, shortly after their arrival, the tragic Dole Pineapple Derby race of August from Oakland to Hawaii almost negated the hard-won gains of 1927. Directly and indirectly, the scramble of ill-prepared contestants for the $35,000 prize money accounted for the deaths of 10 flyers. Only two out of eight starters reached Hawaii. Worldwide public revulsion at the needless loss of life almost ended the Australian challenge until a wealthy American shipping magnate, Captain G. Allan Hancock, backed the venture.

Kingsford-Smith and Ulm purchased the Fokker F. VIIB/3m *Detroiter*, previously owned by Arctic explorer Sir Hubert Wilkins. Renamed the *Southern Cross*, it was fitted out with Whirlwind J-5C engines and the best available blind-flying instruments and radios. To ensure the bull's-eye accuracy required

Lieutenants Albert F. Hegenberger (left) and Lester J. Maitland and their Fokker C-2 transport *Bird of Paradise*. Their 1927 flight from Oakland to Honolulu was superbly planned and executed. However, only two months later American aviation suffered a body blow from the disastrous Dole Air Derby. Flown over the same route, it led to the loss of 10 aircraft and 10 lives, including those lost in prerace preparation.

I reached over and touched her. She was cool to my touch. There was no blinking light on her oxygen! No light on the panel for her oxygen. She wasn't breathing!

Then, flying the airplane with my right hand, I reached over with my left to rub her back and neck. No reaction. I shook hard, rubbed her shoulders and neck, and shook again.

All of a sudden she came back to life, leaping up, almost hitting the roof. "What?"...

She couldn't stay awake, and if you're not careful you don't ever wake up, or you wake up with a headache you have the rest of your life. I worried about this and whether I was in any shape to make sure she was getting oxygen while flying the plane and dodging thunderstorms. If she was dead, what would I do? Land, fly on with a corpse? I wondered, and I felt all alone....

We had underestimated the oxygen. With fatigue and her cold she couldn't absorb enough, so I turned her valve up a little bit. Or did I? I thought. Did I already do that?...

In the trailer there had been nothing to do but wait, nervously, with cups of coffee and jokes. Then a new position was relayed in.

"They're west of the lake already!" Conway Roberts said.

Conway couldn't believe it. He went over to the map and fiddled with the pushpins and then took out his flight computer and went over it....

Then Conway understood what we had done. He suspected it right away: there was a nice curve to the planned course around the south of Lake Victoria on the map, and Conway figured it out. We had just sliced that curve off and gone straight across the north side....

Jeana was stirring now, coming back to life. She had an awful headache, and her stomach was churning. It was still hard for her to stay awake....

I checked the log and pulled out the map. Glancing over at the Omega, I read the coordinates there and plotted them. And then I realized where we were: three quarters of the way past Yaounde to the coast. The mountains! I glanced over at the radar, and they were right there, two big shadows.

The image got me going with a jolt, and I made an immediate left turn of twenty degrees to pull the airplane around Mount Cameroon....

The second mountain, Santa Isabel, was about fifteen miles away on an island, and I made sure we gave it a wide berth as we headed out over the coast, leaving the beautiful small city called Douala behind us, and into the Atlantic.

A few minutes later, at 0030 Z, I radioed for our position and gave a set of coordinates....Somebody went scrambling to the maps to sort out the locations.

"We have you on the map, Dick," Walt radioed back, wondering if we were lost, if the fatigue was getting to me somehow, but trying to sound as if everything were under control.

"And what does that mean?" I said.

Walt was perplexed. "Say again?"

"What does that mean? It means we've made Africa, baby. We've made Africa, and we're on our way home...."

We had always thought Africa would be the hardest, and it was—up till then. For a moment I thought we were home free, and that flying across the dark continent was the greatest thing we had ever done in our lives...never mind that we still had a third of the world to go.

On the ground, aerodromes, navigation beacons, and air traffic and meteorological services supported the new industry.

In 1919, only the rich and daring had had the nerve to climb aboard the first rickety airliners, trusting to luck and the weather. Two decades later, only a matter of money prevented the world from commuting in fast, sophisticated comfort. The jumbo-jet age evolving from World War II would break that final barrier.

Besides pioneering the world's future air routes, the quest to fly farther created and maintained public interest. By fostering confidence in the capabilities of the airplane, long-distance flights eventually encouraged the public to fly and, more important, enticed business people to invest in aviation.

The pioneering men and women who established milestones around the world were the public relations teams of the airplane's formative years. They captured the limelight, fired the world's imagination, and kept the dream alive until design caught up with promise. Today we climb on board an airliner and cross an ocean as casually as our grandparents boarded a train. That is their legacy.

FASTER

AND HIGHER

FASTER AND

The Quest for Speed and Power

JOHN D. ANDERSON, JR.

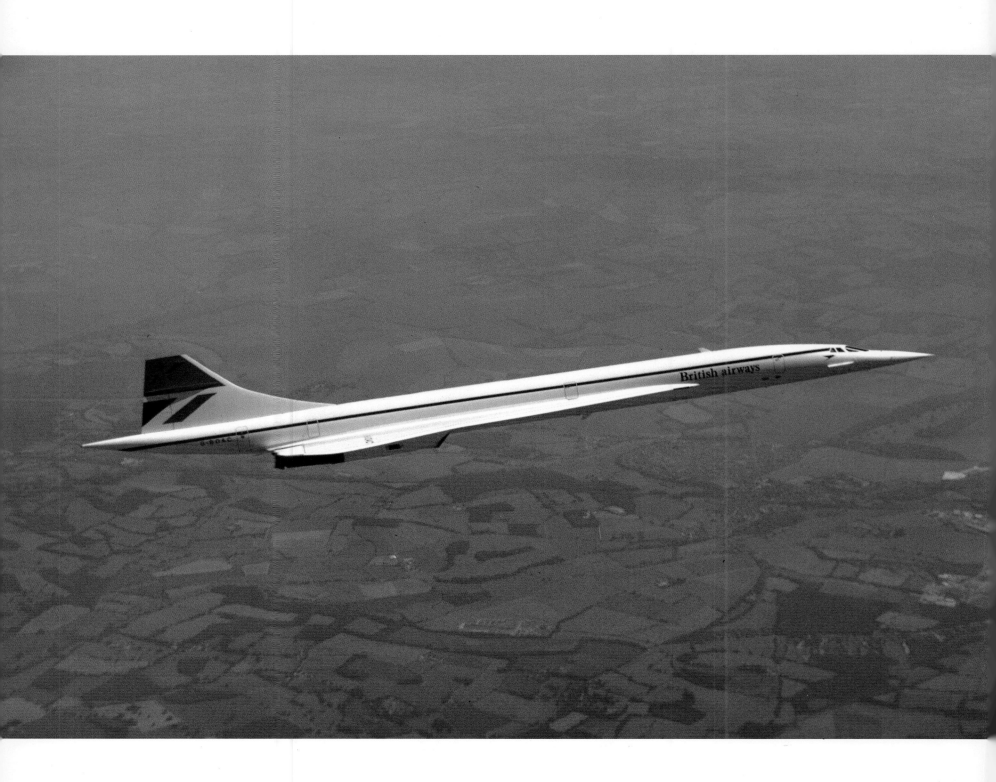

MacROBERTSON AIR RACE OF 1934

A unique air race, considered by some the greatest single sporting event in the history of aviation, was the 11,300-mile MacRobertson race between England and Australia held in 1934. The race was organized as part of the Melbourne centenary celebration and was funded by Sir MacPherson Robertson. The contestants were to take off at Mildenhall in Suffolk, England, make stops at prescribed intermediate locations, and land at Melbourne. The de Havilland Aircraft Company in England designed a unique airplane with the single purpose of winning the MacRobertson Race. The D.H.88 Comet was a sleek, aerodynamically refined twin-engine design powered by two de Havilland Gipsy Six R air-cooled in-line engines of 240 horsepower each. The maximum speed of 237 mph was combined with an exceptionally long range of nearly 3,000 miles, an extremely important asset for this race.

Flying a Comet, Charles W. A. Scott and Tom Campbell Black won the race, starting in England on October 20, 1934, and arriving in Melbourne 70 hours and 59 minutes later. In this case, however, the winner was not nearly

The de Havilland D.H.88 was a special-purpose, long-range racer designed specifically to win the England-to-Australia air race in 1934. The Comet's maximum speed was 237 mph, and the winning Comet covered the distance in 70 hours and 59 minutes with intermediate stops. The Comet subsequently influenced the design of de Havilland's D.H. 91 Albatross four-engine airliner and D.H. 98 Mosquito of World War II. The restored Comet flies again over England.

as significant as the second and third place finishers—the K.L.M. DC-2 *Uiver* and a Boeing 247, both standard production commercial airliners (see Chapter 1).

The importance of the D.H.88 Comet also reached far beyond the MacRobertson Air Race, because from its design came four-engine D.H. 91 Albatross airliner, whose production was cut short by the war, and the famous de Havilland Mosquito, one of the most versatile and unusual aircraft of World War II. Dubbed the "wooden wonder" because of its molded wooden fuselage and wings, the twin-engine "Mossy" came in a wide variety of bomber, fighter, and reconnaissance versions. It flew so high (over 30,000 feet) and so fast (415, and 425 mph in later MK XVI bomber and P.R. 34 reconnaissance versions fitted with two 1,710-horsepower Merlin 76 engines) that it required no defensive armament and packed a terrific punch as a fighter (four 20-mm cannon and four .303-caliber machine guns). Despite its achievements, the Mosquito's wooden construction made it a dead-end aircraft with no postwar future.

DEVELOPING MATURITY: THE LATE 1930s

In the late 1930s, the maturity of the propeller-driven airplane increased rapidly. Just before World War II, airplanes took on a new, more sophisticated look, typified by the Seversky P-35 and the Hughes H-1 racer. The former was a low-wing monoplane with a full engine cowling and retractable landing gear and was powered by a 950-horsepower Pratt & Whitney R-1830-9 radial engine equipped with a geared supercharger and a variable-pitch propeller. Redesigned in 1936 by Alexander Kartveli, Seversky's chief designer, and produced from July 1937 to August 1938, the P-35 had all the features of the fully mature, propeller-driven fighter airplane. Its top speed was very close to 300 mph, obtained more by a low-drag airframe than by high thrust. Even by contemporary standards the P-35 was underpowered, and for this reason the Army Air Corps ordered only 77. Nonetheless, a civilian version, the SEV-S2, won three consecutive Bendix Trophy races from 1937 through 1939.

In 1939, the Seversky Aircraft Company became Republic Aviation

Incorporated. Again under the direction of Kartveli, the design features of the P-35 grew through the intermediate XP-43 Lancer into a new airplane, the Republic P-47 Thunderbolt of World War II. Outfitted with advanced versions of the Pratt & Whitney R-2800 engine that could deliver 2,800 horsepower in its later models, the Thunderbolt became one of the largest, fastest, most rugged, and most heavily armed fighters of the war. A highly advanced experimental version, the XP-47J, set the highest unofficial speed ever recorded for a propeller-driven World War II airplane, achieving 504 mph at 34,450 feet in August 1944.

Contemporary with the P-35, Howard Hughes designed and built the H-1 special-purpose racing aircraft. In the middle 1930s, Hughes aspired to three aviation goals: to break the world's speed record for land planes, to set a transcontinental speed record, and to win a Thompson Trophy air race. To accomplish this, Hughes designed and built a new airplane, the H-1, that had all the elements of the mature, propeller-driven aircraft.

Great attention was given to drag reduction during the design and manufacture of the H-1, including a highly polished surface and screw heads slotted to align with the airflow. Two sets of wings were built for the H-1: a short, 25-foot wing for the high-speed attempt and a longer 32-foot wing for the transcontinental flight. At high speed, induced drag is low, and so the lower aspect-ratio wing had an advantage as a result of lower skin friction drag. On the other hand, for the transcontinental flight, the combined effect of lower average speed and high altitudes accentuated the induced drag; thus, a higher aspect-ratio wing was a better compromise.

With the H-1 racer, Hughes accomplished two of his three goals. On September 14, 1935, he set the world speed record of 352 mph for a land plane, and on January 20, 1937, he set a record by averaging 332 mph in a flight lasting 7 hours and 28 minutes from Burbank, California, to New York City. However, Hughes never won the Thompson Trophy. There were complaints that the H-1 racer represented unfair competition, and Hughes never entered the race. Hughes then returned the H-1 to California, where it sat in storage until 1975, when it was given to the Smithsonian's National Air and Space Museum.

to increase T greatly. The myth of the sound barrier was just that—a myth. An aircraft can fly faster than the speed of sound so long as there is enough thrust to push it through the barrier. The Bell engineers chose the Reaction Motors four-chamber, 6,000-pound-thrust rocket engine for this job.

On Tuesday, October 14, 1947, Yeager flew the X-1 in an attempt to surpass the speed of sound. Yeager was suffering from two broken ribs fractured during a horseback-riding accident the previous weekend, but he told virtually no one. At 10:26 A.M., at an altitude of 20,000 feet, the Bell X-1 was dropped from the belly of a B-29 carrier airplane. It then powered itself to Mach 1.06 at an altitude of 42,000 feet, the first manned supersonic flight in history. Less than a month later, Yeager reached Mach 1.35 in the same airplane. The sound barrier had been penetrated, and the myth was destroyed.

The next major barriers fell to the D-558-2 Skyrocket that Douglas built for the U.S. Navy and NACA as a supersonic research aircraft. Using captured German aerodynamic reports, the D-558 design team, headed by Ed Heinemann, produced a swept-wing rocket and turbojet version of the jet-powered Douglas D-558-1 Skystreak transonic research aircraft. In 1950 Douglas modified the second D-558-2 to take Reaction Motors' 6,000-pound thrust XLR-8-RM-6 rocket motor. On January 26, 1951, Douglas test pilot Bill Bridgeman was accidentally launched from the P2B-1S, a Navy-modified B-29 mother ship, over Edwards Air Force Base, California, and in a dive from 40,000 feet hit Mach 1.28. In six more flights during the summer of 1951, Bridgeman reached Mach 1.79 on June 11, Mach 1.85 on June 23, Mach 1.88 on August 7, and 74,494 feet on August 15. The Skyrocket had flown faster and higher than any manned aircraft ever—what the X-1 had broken, the Skyrocket smashed forever.

Under NACA control, the Skyrocket established a new world's altitude record on August 21, 1953, when Marion Carl reached 83,235 feet. Then, on November 20, 1953, A. Scott Crossfield became the first man to fly at twice the speed of sound when he dove his aircraft from 72,000 feet and reached Mach 2.005, or 1,291 mph. The last Skyrocket was retired in 1956 after accumulating much useful research data on supersonic flight. Appropriately, the record-setting D-558-2 is on display at the National Air and Space Museum with the Bell X-1.

THE CONTINUING QUEST FOR SPEED AND ALTITUDE

The quest for speed was insatiable. On May 25, 1953, the North American F-100 Super Sabre became the first fighter capable of sustained supersonic

The North American F-100 Super Sabre, the first of the U.S. Air Force's "Century series," was the first fighter designed for sustained supersonic flight. It first flew on May 25, 1953. Although it became operational before the end of 1953, a number of accidents and control problems led to modifications that slowed its introduction. Another problem was that pilots had to learn the nuances of supersonic flight. The F-100 had a maximum speed of 864 mph at 35,000 feet. An F-100C of the Air Defense Command is shown in flight near Holloman Air Force Base, New Mexico, in 1967.

The area rule was developed in the early 1950s as a means of reducing drag as an airplane flew through Mach 1. As originally designed, the F-102 Delta Dagger was based on Alexander Lippisch's research on delta wings in Germany and on Convair's experimental XP-92A of 1948. When the initial YF-102 flew at Edwards Air Force Base, California, in October 1953 and January 1954, it exhibited poor performance and was unable to go supersonic. However, Convair undertook a major investigation and soon redesigned the aircraft as the YF-102A, primarily by reducing the cross-sectional area of the fuselage in the wing region to produce the so-called Coke bottle shape, as prescribed by the area rule of NACA's Richard Whitcomb. The YF-102A achieved supersonic speeds on its second test flight, and Convair went on to build 975 Delta Dagger air defense interceptors for the U.S. Air Force from 1953 through 1957. This initial application of Whitcomb's area rule produced a successful supersonic airplane and saved Convair from a major design failure.

Facing page:
Four F-106 Delta Dart supersonic interceptors of the U.S. Air Defense Command

speeds in level flight. It was powered by a Pratt & Whitney J57 turbojet with 16,000 pounds of thrust—four times greater than that of the Lockheed P-80 and three times that of the F-86. The T − D relationship was being stretched significantly simply by the addition of brute thrust.

At the same time, Convair was designing a delta-wing fighter, the F-102, that was having major difficulties breaking the speed of sound; the increase in drag near Mach 1 was simply too great. Fortunately, an aerodynamicist at NACA's Langley laboratory, Richard T. Whitcomb, had been conducting experiments on a unique concept for transonic drag reduction. By reducing the cross-sectional area of the fuselage in the vicinity of the wings, Whitcomb proved that the drag near Mach 1 could be reduced. This principle, called the *area rule*, was incorporated in a modified YF-102, and the airplane readily went supersonic with a maximum speed of 825 mph (Mach 1.25) and into service with the U.S. Air Force as the F-102 Delta Dagger. The follow-on F-102B—later designated the F-106 Delta Dart—was completely redesigned using the area rule to produce a much neater and more aerodynamically efficient aircraft. The F-106 also added a new Pratt & Whitney J75 turbojet engine with 50 percent more thrust that gave it a top speed of 1,525 mph (Mach 2.3) at 36,000 feet. In 1954, Whitcomb received the Collier Trophy for his pioneering work with the area rule, one of the most important advances in high-speed aerodynamics.

In February 1954, the first fighter capable of sustained flight at Mach 2, the Lockheed F-104 Starfigher, made its first appearance. In addition to those built for the U.S. Air Force, large numbers of F-104s were manufactured under license arrangements in Germany, Japan, Canada, Belgium, Italy, and the Netherlands, while the U.S. provided others to Denmark, Norway, Greece, and Turkey. In May 1958, an F-104 set a world's speed record of

1,404 mph as well as an altitude record of 91,243 feet. By the year 1960 supersonic flight was an everyday affair, not just the domain of research aircraft such as the X-1 and Douglas Skyrocket.

The quest for altitude was embodied in a special-purpose military airplane, the Lockheed U-2. Designed with an exceptionally large wing aspect ratio of 14.3, the U-2 was capable of flying at 90,000 feet. However, the quests for altitude and speed were combined in the U-2's successor, the Lockheed SR-71 Blackbird. This too was a special-purpose aircraft for high-altitude, high-speed reconnaissance, but unlike the subsonic U-2, the SR-71 was capable of sustained flight at Mach 3 at an altitude of about 100,000 feet. Designed at the Lockheed "Skunk Works" under Kelly Johnson, the same combination that produced the XP-80 and the U-2, the SR-71 broke new

Facing page:
The Lockheed F-104 Starfighter was the first America's fighter designed for sustained use at Mach 2. This airplane contained the best supersonic aerodynamics: a sharp-nosed slender fuselage and an extremely thin, very-low-aspect-ratio wing to reduce wave drag. In May 1958, on separate flights, the F-104 set a speed record of 1,404 mph, and a record altitude of 91,243 feet. These photos show two F-104As over San Francisco Bay and an F-104 fitted with a refueling probe dropping away from a KC-135 tanker after refueling.

This Lockheed U-2R of the Strategic Air Command's 9th Strategic Reconnaissance Squadron at Beale Air Force Base, California, was a complete redesign of the earlier versions that had emerged from Clarence "Kelly" Johnson's "Skunk Works" as high-altitude (70,000 feet and up) aerial photographic reconnaissance platforms. Used during the mid-1950s mainly by the CIA and the U.S. Air Force's Strategic Air Command to collect photographic intelligence over the Soviet Union, the U-2 was a supersecret aircraft that first came to world attention when a Soviet surface-to-air missile shot down Francis Gary Powers in his U-2B near Sverdlovsk on May 1, 1960. U-2 missions over Cuba in August 1962 confirmed the presence of Soviet intermediate-range ballistic missiles, leading to the Cuban missile crisis.

The SR-71A Blackbird is a further development of the U.S. Air Force's experimental YF-12A interceptor and the CIA's A-12 high-speed, high-altitude reconnaissance aircraft of the late 1950s.

The SR-71A first flew in 1964, entered service with the Strategic Air Command in 1966, and has seen extensive global use ever since. With its sophisticated cameras and sensors, a Blackbird can photograph 100,000 square miles in a single hour while flying at Mach 3 above 80,000 feet.

ground in aerodynamics, propulsion, structures, and materials. It is still the fastest and highest-flying operational aircraft in the world, holding absolute world records for speed over 2,000 mph. The absolute altitude record for jet aircraft, however, belongs to Aleksandr Fedotov and the experimental Mikoyan Ye-266M (MiG-25 prototype), which set a record of 123,523.58 feet on August 31, 1977.

HYPERSONIC FLIGHT: FROM THE X-15 TO THE SPACE SHUTTLE AND THE FUTURE

Once the sound barrier had been broken, it was left far behind. The next goal became manned hypersonic flight at Mach 5 and beyond. This flight regime is characterized not only by high wave drag associated with the strong shock waves but also by high temperatures in the flow around the vehicle, thus introducing aerodynamic heating as a new technological challenge for the designer. With these problems in mind, in 1955 the American government awarded a contract to North American Aviation for the design and construction of three prototypes of a manned hypersonic research airplane, designated the X-15, that was capable of a nominal Mach 7 and a maximum altitude of 264,000 feet—about 50 miles. The X-15 has a basic internal structure made from titanium and stainless steel, but the skin is Inconel X, a nickel alloy capable of withstanding temperatures up to 1,200 degrees Fahrenheit.

The first X-15 rolled out of the North American factory at Los Angeles on October 15, 1958. Vice President Richard M. Nixon was the guest of honor at the rollout ceremonies. The mystique of high-speed airplanes as symbols of national pride (which started with the Schneider Cup races) was alive and well.

The X-15 flight program of 199 flights lasted until October 24, 1968, and was successful in all respects. On July 17, 1962, Major Robert White had zoomed to an altitude record of 314,750 feet, virtually at the edge of the atmosphere. The maximum Mach number achieved was 6.72 during a flight on October 3, 1967, with Air Force Major Pete Knight at the controls. Such flights formed the basis for claims that the X-15 was the Air Force's first manned "space vehicle."

The North American X-15 was the first hypersonic airplane. On October 3, 1967, it achieved Mach 6.72. On July 17, 1962, it had zoomed to an altitude of 314,750 feet. Like the Bell X-1 and Douglas Skyrocket research aircraft before it, the X-15 was carried into launch position by a modified E-52 mother ship.

Starting with the X-15, manned hypersonic airplane flight, although by no means commonplace, became a reality. The X-15 was the test bed from which the Space Shuttle was derived. On April 12, 1981, the NASA's *Columbia* became the first space shuttle to achieve an orbital flight, and on April 14 it returned to Earth, entering the atmosphere as a controlled glider at Mach 25.

The next steps in manned hypersonic flights are now being developed. There are ideas for transatmospheric vehicles—aircraft that will take off like ordinary airplanes from ordinary runways, accelerate through Mach 1, and then literally blast their way to Mach 25 and orbit strictly on the basis of air-breathing propulsion without rocket boosters. These transatmospheric vehicles will then carry out a mission in orbit, after which they will reenter the atmosphere at Mach 25 and, either as gliders or under power, return to a conventional airport. A project to develop such a transatmospheric vehicle in the United States, the National Aerospace Plane Project, was started in 1985 with the goal of producing a hypersonic test vehicle, the X-30. In addition, NASA is looking toward an eventual commercial hypersonic transport and is already conducting research toward this end. Even the idea of a "far" space shuttle is being considered, entailing a space shuttle that will go into very high geosynchronous orbit around Earth or a planetary mission to Mars or other planets and then return to Earth, entering the atmosphere at Mach 36.

The current realities of hypersonic flight are the milestones already attained, and the dreams of transatmospheric missions and vehicles only set out markers for the future. The quest for speed and altitude, which started on December 17, 1903, with a small, fledgling biplane struggling along at 30 mph barely 20 feet above the ground, has now progressed to flight far beyond the outer regions of the atmosphere at speeds of Mach 25 on the way to Mach 36. How proud Wilbur and Orville Wright would be of these achievements that have sprung from that first flight of December 1903, and how exciting the future prospects will be for the Orvilles and Wilburs of the twenty-first century. The many milestones so far laid down in the relentless quest for greater speed and higher altitude in manned, powered flying machines mark one of the crowning achievements of the human race. There is no reason why this quest will not continue indefinitely into the future.

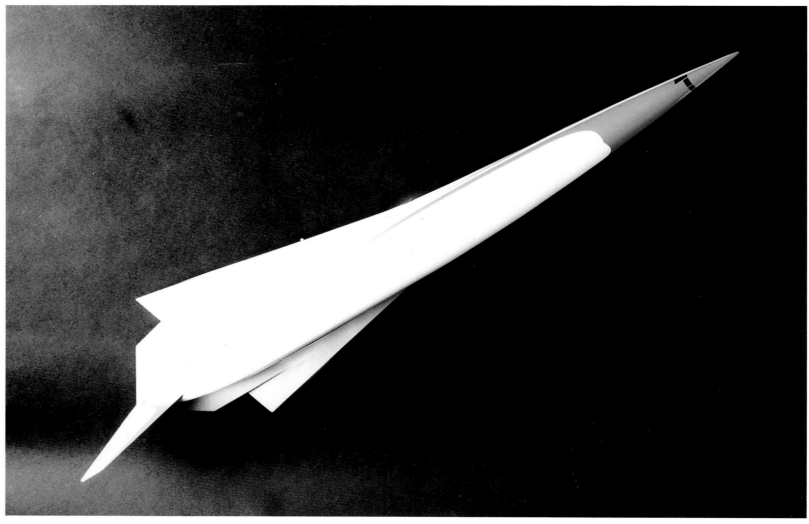

The first man to fly Handley Page's colossal V/1500, Britain's biggest bomber of World War I, was Clifford Prodger, an American living in England who has been called the first freelance test pilot. In one of Prodger's flights in 1918, the V/1500 carried a record 41 passengers. Adventurous passengers sat in the positions of the nose, dorsal, and the tail gunners.

Although 1,000-kilogram (2,200-pound) bombs like this were sometimes dropped from the largest of the German R-planes in World War I, their loads more typically consisted of 12 to 18 100-kilogram (220-pound) bombs.

Given the then adolescent state of aircraft technology, the only way to achieve all these things together and provide the structural weight needed to carry such a heavy payload was to increase wing area. The only acceptable way to give an airplane sufficient wing area yet make it small enough dimensionally so that it could be accommodated on the landing fields that were then available, was to give it two or more wings. Thus, nearly all the big aircraft built early in the century were either biplanes or triplanes.

The most extraordinary World War I airplanes in terms of size were the heavy bombers known as R-planes—"R" standing for Reisenflugzeuge, or "giant airplanes." As manufactured in Germany from 1915 to 1918 by Zeppelin-Staaken (successor of Versuchsbau Gotha-Ost, or V.G.O.), the Allgemeine Elektrizitäts Gesellschaft (A.E.G.), Linke-Hoffmann, and Siemens-Schukert, the majority of R-planes were multi-bay, strut and wire-braced biplanes. They possessed a conventional wooden framework and fabric covering. By the end of the war, however, designers with R-plane experience—notably Claude Dornier—were designing giant monoplane bombers incorporating thick cantilever wings. The plan was to build them of Düraluminium, a high-strength aluminum alloy called duralumin in American usage. After the war, Adolf Rohrbach, who had worked with Dornier, designed for Zeppelin-Staaken such a metal monoplane, the 19,000-pound E.4/20 Giant, which

Adolf Rohrbach's Zeppelin-Staaken E.4/20 required extremely heavy bulkheads in the fuselage to support its huge semicantilever monoplane wing of 138½ feet. Built into the very thick (ribbed and covered with duralumin) wing structure were four 245-horsepower Maybach engines. Inside each nacelle was a seat for a mechanic, who could reach the engine by crawling through a tunnel leading from the fuselage. The E.4/20 was a major advance in aircraft design using *Düraluminium* metal. Fearing its possible use as a bomber and the advance it represented, the Allied Control Commission in Germany ordered the E.4/20 destroyed in November 1922.

The Zeppelin-Staaken R-planes were powered by four Maybach engines mounted in streamlined nacelles between the wings. The nacelles were easily accessible from the fuselage so that crew-members could work on the engines and take care of other mechanical problems.

The German SSW R.VIII was the largest aircraft built during World War I. The large fuselage housed the engines, which drove two two-bladed tractor propellers and two four-bladed pushers. Note the absence of engines between the wings.

could carry 12 to 18 passengers up to 740 miles at a cruising speed of 124 mph.

What made the R-planes exceptional was not just their size but also the requirement to maintain and repair the engines *in flight*. For some of the German giants, such as the twin-engine A.E.G. R.I and the Linke-Hoffmann R.I and R.II, the designer had situated the engines fore and aft in the fuselage and then had used shafts, pulleys, gears, and clutches to drive propellers located outboard on struts between the wings. Others, including most of the planes built by Zeppelin-Staaken, possessed conventional engine-propeller arrangements set between the wings, but they also had ladders so that the crew members could climb out, stand on the ladder, and change spark plugs while flying.

The idea of working on engines in flight seems astonishing and even strange today, but engine technology was too unreliable in those days for airplanes to complete long-distance missions without in-flight maintenance and repair. Besides changing spark plugs, the wing-walking and ladder-climbing daredevils could also accomplish the greasing of rocker arm bearings and other simple tasks.

The R-planes were not unique in this. Many of the planes that set early endurance records had catwalks so that crew members could go outside

With room to spare, 34 men stand in front of the 128-foot wingspan of the Handley-Page V/1500. Immediately above and behind the pilot, in a tank built to conform with the contour of the upper fuselage, rested the 1,000 Imperial gallons of fuel for a round trip bombing mission against Berlin. Beneath the fuel tank, on racks in the lower half of the fuselage, hung a bomb load weighing as much as 7,500 pounds. Although the Royal Air Force ordered 225 of the huge airplanes, only three V/1500s had reported for action by the Armistice in November 1918.

Facing page (top):
The Boeing 247 that first entered service with United Air Lines early in 1933 was a sleek, twin-engined, low-wing monoplane of stressed-skin construction that was truly the first of today's commercial airliners. The fully enclosed cabin had room for 10 passengers, two pilots, and a steward. Its appearance prompted TWA to ask Douglas to develop what became the DC-2 and then DC-3. The 247 was restored in the early 1980s and is displayed in the Boeing Museum of Flight in Seattle.

Facing page (bottom):
The quality of the ride between London and Paris improved significantly in 1931 with the introduction of the Handley Page H.P.42 Hannibal. Slow but reliable, the safe and comfortable biplane served throughout the 1930s on British Imperial Airways routes to Europe, Egypt, India, and central Africa. When World War II started, it served briefly as a troop transport.

and examine the engines. Most of the large, multiengine aircraft, such as the Do X, had this feature. Even in the Boeing 314 flying boat of the late 1930s, the giant Convair B-36, and the Lockheed Constitution, a mechanic could crawl out into the engine nacelles and perform minor repairs on the accessory end of the engine while in flight.

Because these large airplanes required the combined power of more than one engine both to lift off and to stay in the air, everything possible had to be done to prevent loss of power. If they lost even one engine, many of these planes could not continue to fly safely and had to land. The 30,000-pound-gross-weight Handley Page V/1500, built by the British in 1918 for the purpose of bombing Berlin but never used in combat, possessed four Rolls-Royce Eagle VIII engines of 360 horsepower each, two tractor and two pusher. The huge biplane simply would not fly if it lost an engine.

Fighting for Control

Having the power of all the engines was one requirement; controlling that power was another. What caused the fatal crash of England's Tarrant Tabor triplane bomber on its maiden flight at Farnborough in May 1919 was the lack of such control caused by the poor arrangement of its six 500-horsepower Napier Lion engines. Four of the engines were in tandem on each side of the fuselage; each tandem drove a tractor and a pusher propeller. The other two were above, between the top two wings, driving tractor propellers. After taxiing out on the four lower engines, Sgt. Pilot "Dusty" Dunn opened up the two upper units for takeoff. The coupling moment caused the big triplane to nose over and catch fire, and both Dunn and his copilot died.

Pilots and aeronautical engineers learned a lot from such tragedies. Unfortunately, some of them learned how to do a better job of coaxing such aircraft into the air rather than ceasing to make them. In truth, only rarely have designers and engineers determined the "size" of their airplanes; usually, that has been done by prospective customers with more money than good sense. In the early 1930s, just a few years before the state-of-the-art Boeing 247 and Douglas DC-2 airliner were designed in the United States, Handley Page completed work on two large biplane passenger airliners: the 38-seat H.P.42 Hannibal and the H.P.45 Heracles. In comparison to the sleek new Boeing or Douglas airplanes, they were technological dinosaurs.

THE JUNKERS G38

One of the most remarkable big airplanes of the interwar period was the Junkers G38 of 1929. Although it weighed 52,911 pounds and had a wingspan over 144 feet, it was not really the size of the German transport that was extraordinary; it was the way that Junkers integrated the aircraft's size into a novel structure. Built primarily of metal, the G38 possessed wings so thick that small passenger cabins could be built into them. More importantly, the monoplane wings were thick enough to house the aircraft's four powerful engines. Besides the aerodynamic advantages of burying the engine nacelles in the leading edge of the wings, this meant that crew members could get to and attend to these engines in flight without risking their lives by going outside, as R-plane mechanics had done during World War I.

Unfortunately, so much engine power was needed to lift the G38 into the air that it could accommodate only 34 passengers: three in each of two cabins in the wing root, two in the nose of the fuselage, and 26 in the main fuselage cabin.

Junkers produced only two G38s, and Lufthansa, the German national airline, operated both. Neither plane lasted for long: one of them, the *Deutschland*, crashed in 1936, and the other, the *Generalfeldmarschall von Hindenburg*, was destroyed by an RAF bombing raid in 1940.

The Junkers G 38.

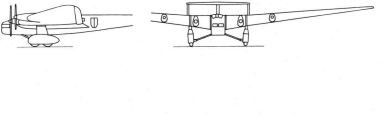

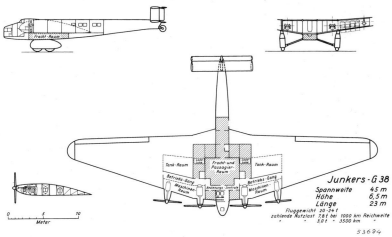

The Junkers G 38.

The Junkers G 38.

The Junkers G 38.

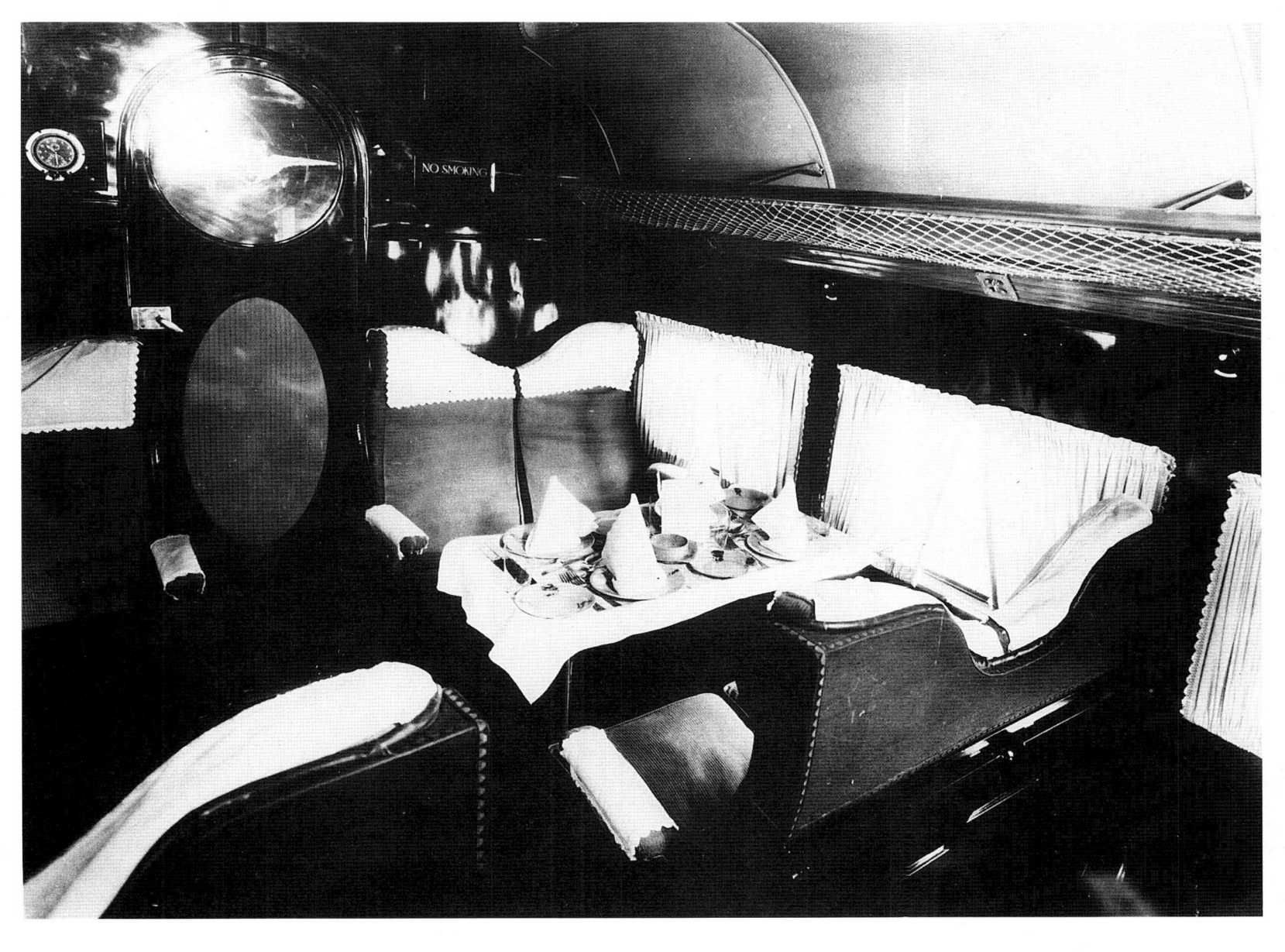

The H.P.42 was, however, one of the world's first four-engine airliners to enter scheduled service, along with the Fokker F.32 of 1929.

A gigantic biplane with a 130-foot wingspan, the H.P.42 cruised at a leisurely top speed of 100 mph on the power of four Bristol Jupiter engines, assuming there was no head wind. Two of the engines were on the upper wing, similar to the catastrophic arrangement on the Tarrant Tabor. Fortunately, when an H.P.42 pilot started a takeoff run, he was smart enough not to open up the top engines until the airplane had developed enough speed so that its tail could hold it down. This stopped the airplane from nosing over as the Tabor had done. The pilot could then open up the upper engines.

Given this dangerous condition, the airplane's lack of speed, and its overall obsolescent design in comparison to the modern airliners that were just appearing in the United States, it is astonishing how much success the H.P.42 enjoyed. A fleet of eight aircraft was used by British Imperial Airways from 1931 to 1939, and not a single passenger died or was seriously hurt in one. Moreover, passengers liked flying in them. Igor Sikorsky once remarked that British airliners were slow; even the flights between London and Paris took two and a half hours, so that the passengers would have time to enjoy a meal. Inside the H.P.42 there was enough room, and almost always enough time, to be served substantial and elegant meals. For many people, however, that leisurely pace beat spending all day on the train and crossing the unpredictable Channel by boat.

The operation of multiengine aircraft continued to be a problem for years to come, even when the airplanes were not very large. During the

The H.P.42's cruising speed was only 100 mph. When the much faster Armstrong Whitworth Ensign (170 mph) and the de Havilland D.H.91 Albatross began replacing the Hannibals in the late 1930s, many passengers on Imperial Airways complained that the flight from London to Paris no longer gave them their money's worth.

takeoff and climb of the Ford Tri-Motor, a moderate-size (13,500 pounds) high-wing monoplane produced for airline service between 1926 and 1933, the pilot and copilot had to keep both feet on the rudder pedals because they had no trim tab. If the Tri-Motor lost an engine, it took both men to hold the airplane straight.

Another serious problem has been the nervous exhaustion suffered by pilots. With the incredible size of some of the structures, the terribly high inertia and control forces, and the slow rates of response, the pilots' fear was totally justifiable. Many of these big airplanes were dangerously sluggish. For example, according to Cecil Lewis, the Royal Air Force's Handley Page 0/400 twin-engine bomber (gross weight 13,300 pounds) of 1918 behaved "like a lorry in the air. When you decided to turn left, you pushed over the controls, went and had a cup of tea and came back to find the turn just starting."

Slow-to-respond controls in combination with other extreme stresses facing pilot and machine led to many catastrophic failures. After several successful bombing raids to the eastern front, Zeppelin's first R-plane, the 21,000-pound V.G.O. I, crashed late in 1915, killing the crew. A little later, even before it could be delivered to the German Army, so too did the V.G.O. II. In early 1917, one of the Linke-Hoffmann giants broke up in the air when the wings collapsed. A year later, the A.E.G. R.I. also broke up in midair, when a propeller failed, killing the crew. In all, Germany produced over 50 R-series heavy bombers during the war. Only a handful were brought down in combat. A greater number were destroyed in some type of accident, like many of the other airplanes of World War I, which had similarly high accident rates. A few of these airplanes survived the war to give "joyrides" to naive paying passengers.

In the following decades, new technologies such as servo tabs, full-

A Ford Tri-motor rebuilt by American Airlines in the early 1960s hangs from the ceiling in the National Air and Space Museum's Air Transportation Gallery just in front of a Delta DC-3.

The 25,000-pound German Linke-Hofmann R.I. of 1917 was capable of some excellent maneuvers, but it was slow to respond to controls and very difficult to land because the pilot sat so high—near the top of a fuselage that was over 20 feet high.

power control systems, and aerodynamic balancing of control surfaces ultimately alleviated much of the difficulty of manually piloting these giants. But even with the development of electronic and automatic controls, it would still not be easy. On big commercial airliners today, the time it takes for the airplane to respond to controls still tends to be significantly longer than is the case for small airplanes.

EARTHBOUND LIMITATIONS

An important factor in the high accident rate of big airliners in the early days was the small size and poor condition of landing fields and their runways. Most airports amounted to no more than an open grass field with a few flimsy hangars in one corner. The usual shape of the field was square or rectangular so that a pilot could head the machine into the wind regardless of its direction. In metropolitan areas, it was also common for airports to be surrounded by buildings and power lines. Small wonder that the pilots of these colossal machines had serious qualms about takeoffs and landings.

Runways were made of sod or cinder or were nonexistent, even at military airfields. As late as the mid-1930s, the U.S. Army Air Corps base at Langley Field, Virginia, was only a big grass field with no runways. The only artificially hard surface was a wide concrete taxi ramp about a half mile long running in front of a row of hangars. Occasionally, test pilots from the NACA (National Advisory Committee for Aeronautics) Langley Aeronautical Laboratory, which shared the use of Langley Field with the Army, would use this ramp as a takeoff runway for small experimental aircraft. Concrete runways did not begin to appear even at the most vital military airfields until the late 1930s and early 1940s. Hard runways at major commercial airports had come only a few years earlier.

Although less directly related to flight safety, even the size and shape of hangars could work against large airplanes. During World War I, the Royal Air Force told its aircraft manufacturers that their airplanes had to fit inside the standard RAF hangar. This gave designers a fit. Handley Page, for example, had to find a way of folding up the big wings of the 0/400 bomber until they

The Handley Page 0/400 wings were foldable so that it could fit in the standard RAF hangar of the time.

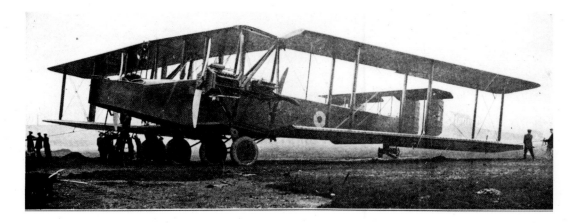

The Short Stirling was an early mainstay of the RAF Bomber Command's night bomber offensive against Germany. An otherwise excellent aircraft with a payload capacity of 14,000 pounds of bombs at 590 miles, the Stirling was hampered by the shortening of its wings, which limited its service ceiling. This Stirling Mark III in its matte black night bombing paint scheme entered service in 1942, but by mid-1943 the Stirling was largely outmoded and had been replaced by Lancasters and Halifaxes.

The only DC-4E ever built arrives at New York's Floyd Bennett Field on June 1, 1939, after completing its test flight from Santa Monica, California. The redesigned triple tail is clearly visible.

almost rested flush to the fuselage. As one critic of this questionable dictate has observed, the RAF apparently felt that it was "more cost effective to complicate and perhaps compromise the aircraft than to build new hangars."

This particular shortsightedness continued to hamper British aircraft designers throughout the interwar period. When the Air Ministry issued its Specification B.12/36 for new heavy bombers in July 1936, it required that the aircraft's wingspan fit within the 100-foot opening of the standard large hangars. Because of this, Short Brothers limited their four-engine Stirling to a 99-foot wingspan. To obtain the necessary wing area to keep a reasonable wing loading for a bomber with a gross weight of 70,000 pounds, the chord was increased. In turn, this produced a very low aspect ratio wing that limited the big bomber's ceiling to 17,000 feet and severely affected its operational usefulness when war broke out in 1939.

The same thing held true in many other cases. Engineers had to reduce the overall height of both the Douglas DC-4E and the Lockheed L.049 Constellation, making it easier to push the aircraft under the lintel of hangar doorways, by employing a low triple-tail arrangement instead of one tall tail. Furthermore, the sizing of a number of military aircraft, including the McDonnell F-4 Phantom, has been done to accommodate these airplanes to the dimensions of the elevator that brings them to the flight deck on an aircraft carrier and to the limited storage space available on an aircraft carrier's hangar deck.

MORE WINGS, MORE WHEELS

Given these earthbound limitations on the physical dimensions of aircraft, designers did their best to come up with aerodynamic configurations that offered the greatest possible lift for a given length, height, and wingspan. During World War I, this was one of the factors that led to the triplane phenomenon.

The largest triplanes of the war were built by Gianni Caproni and used by the Italian Army (along with a number of Caproni biplanes) to bomb targets inside the Austro-Hungarian Empire. To make such raids, these airplanes not only had to make round-trip flights of over 500 miles but also had to cross the Alps.

The largest of the Caproni triplanes was the CA 42. One of the special design features required by its phenomenal size was the main landing gear, which consisted of eight wheels in two groupings of four. The idea behind such an arrangement was to help prevent the aircraft from becoming stuck in muddy fields by distributing its 17,700 pounds (MTOW) evenly across the 96.4-foot wingspan.

Just as large people often have trouble with their feet, large airplanes often have trouble with their landing gear. Here again, the criterion for what is large is weight. To modern aeronautical engineers, the problem of designing an efficient landing gear for a large airplane can be as vexing as it was 70 years ago to Caproni. The only experimental 162,000-pound Douglas XB-19 heavy bomber of the late 1930s had two huge wheels and exerted such ground pressure that it broke through concrete taxiways and aprons. The Convair XB-36, one of the largest piston-engine aircraft ever built, carried its full weight of 330,000 pounds on two 110-inch wheels. The ground pressure exerted by the prototype's wheels was so great that it badly cracked or broke through concrete runways, taxiways, and aprons. Convair engineers quickly changed to dual four-wheel bogie main undercarriages with the YB-36 and the production models. Even with the weight well distributed, the runway foundations at airfields built for B-36 operations,

It took 12 years for an aircraft to surpass the gross weight of the Dornier Do X of 1929. That aircraft was the Douglas XB-19, a 162,000-pound all-metal low-wing monoplane experimental strategic bomber that flew for the first time in 1941. Although this was the only XB-19 ever built, it served as a flying test bed, providing important data that were incorporated into the designs of the Boeing B-29 and Consolidated B-36. It was the largest American aircraft until the appearance of the B-36 in August 1946.

A mechanic works on one of the 110-inch wheels of the main landing gear on an XB-36.

One of the XB-19's two huge wheels breaks through the taxiway.

such as those at Limestone Air Force Base, Maine, had to be six feet thick to withstand the weight and constant pounding.

Lockheed rediscovered this problem in the 1960s, when its engineers were working out plans for the undercarriage of the 764,500-pound C-5 military transport. Supporting that kind of weight was going to take exceptionally sturdy feet—a total of 28 wheels.

But what really complicated the design of the C-5, as it had with the B-36 and B-52, was the airplane's *footprint pressure*, that is, the unit loading of the wheels on the runway. Air Force requirements called for the airplane to operate off a hard-surfaced runway and then land on an undeveloped

The C-5A Galaxy's complex of wheels gave it the capability to operate anywhere in the world.

A technological development essential to the construction of huge aircraft has been the creation of large forges, presses, jigs, milling machines, and other machine tools. Here a Lockheed machinist stands next to a 3,200-pound, 24-foot aluminum alloy rib fabricated by a 50,000-ton press for the C-5A. Eighteen of these forgings are milled down to 338 pounds and then used to complete the airplane's main frame structure. At Lockheed-Georgia's plant, finished and treated members can be seen in place forming the skeleton of a new C-5A that awaits the main wing center section.

Facing page:
Today the wide variety of machine tools including presses 10 times heavier than the 5,000-ton Lake Erie press of 1941, produce large structural members of aircraft.

gravel or sod field in the third world. To meet this challenge, Lockheed came up with a very unusual and ingenious system in which each one of the airplane's 28 tires could be inflated or deflated in flight. That way, when the giant Galaxy transport was about to land on a soft field, the crew could reduce the pressure in the tires automatically.

Fortunately, the designers of the R-planes earlier in the century had not faced this requirement; otherwise, some poor acrobatic mechanic would have been ordered to slide off the lower wing and let air out of the tires manually.

"WHERE THERE'S A WILL, THERE'S A WAY"

Nothing in the history of technology illustrates the truth of this adage better than the story of large aircraft design. No matter what the barriers blocking the development of successful airplanes of enormous size, the desire for size always seemed to win out.

As for the square-cube law, what invalidated it time and time again were changes in design philosophy brought on by the development of new technologies. As F.A. Cleveland pointed out in his analysis of size effects in aircraft design, "technological advances have enabled consistently more progress in the size of aircraft than the square-cube law implies."

A major contributing factor to the defeat of the law has been the very significant increase in the stresses that can be maintained in an aircraft structure. This has been due partly to new and much improved materials and partly to the development of huge presses and machine tools to forge and mill parts of the airframe and skin. Specifically, the changeover from wood and fabric to aluminum and aluminum alloys, stainless steel and reinforced plastics, and recently to chemical composites has greatly affected the strength and weight of aircraft. Moreover, the huge presses, milling machines, routers, and electrochemical milling (ECM) processes now in common practice in airframe manufacturing did not exist to produce airframe structures of sufficient strength and size for assembly. Today, huge forging presses of up to 50,000 tons and extrusion presses can turn out complete fuselage frames, spar booms, root ribs, landing gear shock struts, and larger parts up to 50 by 30 feet as single pieces.

Based on his wartime experience with larger bombers, Gianni Caproni built the CA 60 *Trans-aereo* in 1920 and 1921. An enormous flying boat with nine huge wings in three triplane arrangements, powered by eight Liberty engines, this 55,115-pound airplane actually made one short flight over Lake Maggiore on March 4, 1921, before crashing into the water and suffering considerable damage to its hull. Caproni's idea was to determine whether a larger wing area would solve the problem of designing large airplanes. The CA 60 scored an early postwar "triple": the largest airplane of its time, the first triple triplane, and the first airplane designed to carry 100 passengers on trans-Atlantic routes.

Another factor in the defeat of the square-cube law has been the development of effective high-lift systems. Beginning in the late 1920s, the integration of features such as wing flaps and slots made possible by wind tunnel testing has enabled designers to increase their *wing loadings* (the weight per unit of wing area) by a considerable amount. When the wing loadings went up, it generally meant that the size of the wings could be kept down. This is why the wing of the C-5A is not that much bigger than that of the Dornier Do X. Higher wing loadings by themselves would have increased takeoff runs and landing speeds. What effective high-lift systems made possible were higher wing loadings without the need for monstrously large wings or runways 5 to 10 miles long. With such lifting systems, the designer no longer needed to add on a great amount of wing area, as the World War I designers did, by building biplanes and triplanes.

The square-cube rule aside, there was still the problem of the landing field's finite area to overcome. One possible way around it was to employ the broad unobstructed surface of water. As in the case of Caproni's eight-engine triple triplane CA 60 *Transaereo* of 1921, the Dornier Do X, the Latécoère 631, the Boeing 314, the Saunders-Roe SARO Princess, the Hughes-Kaiser H-4, and Norman Bel Geddes's hypothetical 700-ton super airliner, some of the world's largest aircraft over the years have turned out to be flying boats.

Boats in the Sky

The flying boat was a different type of machine, or so it seemed to many people. Two of its most important advantages were that it could take off and alight on the boundless sea rather than within the confines of an airfield and that it could be moored in only slightly protected harbors without the need for huge hangar accommodations. Another advantage was that it did not have the aerodynamic and structural nuisances of an undercarriage, relying instead for landing on a widely distributed water plane area. In the minds of some designers, this makes the flying boat a more "natural" creature, because there is nothing in nature with wheels.

In the minds of others, the flying boat's biggest advantage was its suitability for crossing the oceans. In reality, any plane could do that; the seaplane's advantage would be seen when it *failed* to cross an ocean. Then, unlike other airplanes, it could alight at sea, rest "safely," and even take off again.

The goal of the first really large flying boat, the Curtiss H *America* of 1913, was to be the first to fly across the Atlantic and thus grab the London *Daily Mail's* £10,000 prize. Although preparations for this ambitious flight were canceled when the war came, for the British in particular the war meant that there was an urgent military requirement for long-range naval patrol aircraft to use against German submarines. The Royal Navy Air Service (RNAS) took over the *America*, built some additional H-4s as Small Americas, and then ordered a number of H-8/H-12 Large Americas and H-16 Curtiss flying boats. From them, the RNAS evolved a series of "F" flying boats built at the Admiralty's air station at Felixstowe. The all-up weight of one of the later "F" boats, a triplane nicknamed the Felixstowe Fury, was 23,400 pounds. In 1919, this plane, overloaded with fuel, crashed on takeoff from Plymouth on its way to a nonstop flight to Lisbon.

In one of the most historic flights ever made, also in 1919, one of the U.S. Navy's Curtiss NC flying boats, the 27,386-pound NC-4, made it all the way across the Atlantic Ocean to Plymouth, England, albeit in a series of hops via

A U.S. Navy Curtiss H-16 flying boat on patrol.

The Curtiss NC-4 flying boat that Commander A. C. Read flew across the Atlantic in May 1919 was one of only four NC class flying boats to serve in the U.S. Navy during and after World War I.

Sikorsky's 38,000-pound S-42 flying boats allowed Pan American Airways to develop its Caribbean routes and explore routes across the Pacific and Atlantic for commercial aviation.

THE COMPOSITE: ONE WAY TO BEAT THE DISTANCE PROBLEM

The Short-Mayo composite aircraft of 1938 is an example of early attempts to overcome the need for refueling stops. The large, launching aircraft was a short S.21 Empire-class flying boat named *Maia*. The small floatplane, a Short S.20 *Mercury*, would separate once safely airborne and fly to its destination; the mothership would return home. The designers intended to develop a viable trans-Atlantic mail run. Between

July 20 and 21, 1938, the Mercury, piloted by Captain D.C.T. Bennett, later an Air Vice Marshal with Bomber Command, completed the first commercial crossing of the North Atlantic by a heavier-than-air craft when it flew nonstop from Foynes, Northern Ireland, to Montreal, Canada, and then on to Port Washington, New York. That was its only flight to New York; the following year Pan Am's Clippers went into regular service.

At left and above:

The Short-Mayo composite aircraft.

Newfoundland, the Azores, and Lisbon. As any visitor knows who has seen the restored NC-4 at the U.S. Naval Air Museum in Pensacola, Florida, the most striking physical dimension of the aircraft is not its weightiness (it is hard to see weight) but its massive wing area. At 2,380 square feet, it is not much smaller (only about 18 percent) than the Boeing 707 jet transport. But even its weight is impressive; at 27,386 pounds, its gross weight exceeded that of the Douglas DC-3 of 15 years later by over 2,000 pounds.

Although the United States, Germany, and Japan were also very active, the country that had the most compelling reason to specialize in the construction and operation of flying boats between the wars was Great Britain. The British had a greater need for them because its far-flung empire included remote and forbidding terrain, far from the home island, where it was difficult to build airfields but where rivers, lakes, and harbors were abundant.

In the 1930s, as land planes became larger and heavier, but with few airfields capable of handling them, the flying boat enjoyed great success. With a fleet of Short C-Class flying boats, Imperial Airways moved passengers in comfort and style from London to South Africa, Egypt, and India and on to

Construction of a Boeing 314 flying boat on the huge assembly jig at Boeing's plant in Seattle, Washington. To speed production and cut costs for what was in 1938 the largest aircraft in the world, Boeing developed several new processes and methods of fabrication.

Singapore, Hong Kong, and Australia. Pan American Airways used Sikorsky's S-40 in its Caribbean service and then made trans-Atlantic and even trans-Pacific flights in its progressively larger four-engine Sikorsky S-42, Martin M-130, and Boeing 314 Clippers. Greater Japan Air Lines used the impressive Kawanishi H6K flying boats to fly the home islands as well as to connect them with vital port cities on the Asian mainland.

During World War II, flying boats of all sizes played an important role in maritime antisubmarine patrols and long-range reconnaissance. While the Short Sunderlands and twin-engine Consolidated PBY Catalinas of the RAF's Coastal Command hunted German U-boats in the Bay of Biscay and on the north Atlantic approaches to the British Isles, U.S. Navy Catalinas served in all theaters, especially the Pacific. The same vast operating distances in the Pacific that had spawned the Martin M-130 and Boeing 314 in the 1930s produced two of the largest naval flying boats of the war years—the Kawanishi H8K (gross weight 68,000 pounds, range 4,475 miles) and the Martin JRM-1 Mars (gross weight 145,000 pounds, range 4,700 miles). The five Mars JRM-1 and one JRM-2 flying boats that were built saw limited wartime duty as cargo carriers, but after the war they were used extensively as "water bombers" against forest fires. The 167 Kawanishis produced during the war saw heavy duty in transport and antisubmarine work.

Besides a comfortable dining salon, the Boeing 314 offered passengers the luxury of a private drawing room and separate dressing rooms and toilets. When the *Yankee Clipper* opened Pan Am's service along the north Atlantic route from Port Washington, New York, to Southampton, England, in July 1939 with 17 passengers, the fare was $375 one-way and $675 round-trip.

Facing page (bottom):
In service with Pan American Airways, the Boeing Clippers usually carried no more than two dozen passengers and had to make intermediate stops for refueling. With a full load of 74 passengers, the aircraft's maximum range was only about 1,900 miles. With 24 passengers and a much lighter overall load, the Clippers had a maximum range of over 2,400 miles. Boeing built six 314s and six 314As.

Some Great Flying Boats

Aircraft/Year	Wingspan (feet)	Length (feet)	Gross Weight (pounds)	Cruising Speed (mph)	Range (miles)
Dornier Do X (1929)	157.5	131.3	105,820	134	1,056
Sikorsky S-42 (1934)	114.2	64.2	38,000	170	750
Martin M-130 (1934)	130.0	90.9	52,252	163	2,400
Boeing 314 (1938)	152.0	106.0	84,000	184	2,400
Short S. 23 C (1936)	114	88	40,500	164	760
Short Sunderland V (1943)	112.8	85.3	60,000	134	2,980
Kawanishi H6K2 (1938)	131.2	84.1	35,274	150	2,567
Martin JRM-1 Mars (1944)	200.0	123.2	145,000	153	4,700
Saunders-Roe Princess (1952)	219.5	148	330,000	360	5,270

Only six Martin Mars flying boats were built. Designed in 1938 as a patrol bomber (XPB2M-1) for the U.S. Navy, the modified version (JRM-1) served primarily as a cargo aircraft in the Pacific. The Navy sometimes called the Martin Mars the "flying Liberty ship."

According to a Martin Company publicity release, the 200-foot wingspan of the Mars was so long that a Piper Cub could land on it.

The 45-foot-tall, 145,000-pound Martin Mars dwarfs its fellow amphibian, the Grumman Widgeon. Today, two of the Mars flying boats are used in Canada as water bombers to fight forest fires. The aircraft can refill by flying across a lake and scooping up the water.

EXIT FLYING BOATS, ENTER FOUR-ENGINE LAND PLANES

Excluding Howard Hughes's H-4 Hercules, the so-called *Spruce Goose* venture, the largest flying boat ever built actually flew, and flew very well. The 330,000-pound Saunders-Roe SR.45 SARO Princess was intended by the British Overseas Airways Corporation (BOAC) for luxury service on trans-Atlantic routes between England and New York and first flew in August 1952. Severe technical problems with the gearboxes and contrarotating propellers for its ten 3,780-horsepower Bristol Proteus engines, escalating development and production costs—an all too familiar story for such large aircraft—a cost-conscious British government, and BOAC's move away from large flying

At 330,000 pounds, the Saunders-Roe SRO45 SARO Princess of 1952 outweighed by 20 tons the Bristol Brabazon, which was then Britain's biggest land plane. Although construction of three of these large flying boats with the "double-bubble" hull was started, only one was completed and flown. BOAC backed out of its commitment to use the Princess in 1951, and by the time it flew in 1953, it had no future.

HOWARD HUGHES'S *SPRUCE GOOSE*

Howard Hughes's famous eight-engine H-4 Hercules flying boat of 1947, dubbed the *Spruce Goose*, was the largest aircraft built to its time. The original proposal for the big, 400,000-pound wooden flying boat, with its spectacular 320-foot wingspan, came from within the U.S. government. The idea, which surfaced not long after Pearl Harbor, was to build a cargo and troop carrier that did not require critical wartime materials; in other words, that substituted wood for metal. The steelmaker and shipbuilder Henry J. Kaiser picked up on the idea, and brought Hughes in as an aviation expert. Kaiser's shipyards were building Liberty ships at the rate of one a day, so he thought he might as well produce a large cargo-carrying airplane.

As Hughes kept meddling in the design, making things more complicated and causing lost time, Kaiser backed out. An urgent government project in 1942, the Hughes flying boat had lost all priority by 1944. When Hughes flew the H-4 for the one, and only, time on November 2, 1947, it lifted only 33 feet off the surface of Los Angeles harbor and flew about a mile before settling on the water. It was returned to its massive hangar and never flew again.

Hughes's motives for making things so complicated are not clear. They seem to have revolved around his idea for an "aerial freighter beyond anything Jules Verne could have imagined." It is possible he flew it that once just to prove that something that big could fly.

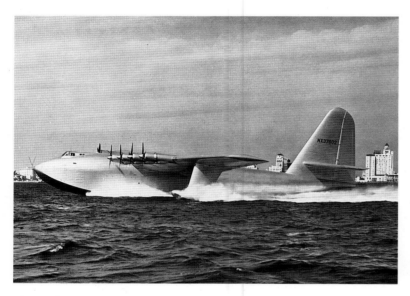

On November 2, 1947, the Hercules made its only flight—and that may have been an accident. When his chief designer asked Hughes, who was at the controls, whether he meant to lift it off the water, Hughes replied, "You'll never know." Today, the *Spruce Goose* is on public exhibition in Long Beach, California.

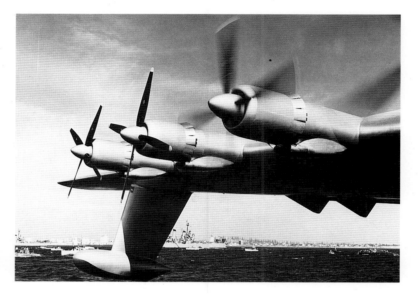

Powering the *Spruce Goose* were eight Pratt & Whitney R-4360 Wasp Major radial air-cooled engines. Each engine had 28 cylinders and generated 3,000 horsepower, every bit of which was necessary to lift the 400,000-pound aircraft off the water.

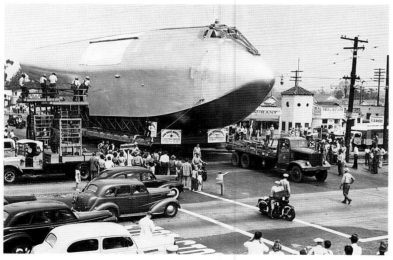

It has been said that not a single scratch was put on any of the big sections of the H-4 Hercules as they were moved very slowly from the factory in Culver City to the assembly site in Long Beach, California, in mid-1946.

Although he thought big, Howard Hughes paid careful attention to the smallest details. The eccentric Hughes would sit for hours in the cockpit of his great wooden flying boat deliberating the design of the control and the instrument panel. Unfortunately, as a perfectionist, he could not make up his mind, and his many delays finally caused a Senate committee to look into the project.

The North American B-45 Tornado was the first jet-powered bomber to enter the U.S. Air Force inventory after World War II. A total of 139 B/RB-45s were built for the Air Force.

could make such major compensations for the adverse effects of size. Thus, when the first jet airplanes are compared with today's jets, they appear rather small. But in comparison to many aircraft of the preceding years, they were indeed very large.

The first jets were all military airplanes, and the largest ones, of course, were bombers. The first jet-powered bomber to be put into production in the United States, North American's B-45 Tornado of 1947, weighed 95,558 pounds, 28,000 pounds less than the Boeing B-29 that dropped the atomic bombs on Japan but 30,000 pounds more than the B-17G Flying Fortress. The dimensions of the B-45's wing were also smaller than that of the B-29: a span of 89.0 feet and an area of 1,175 square feet compared with 141.3 feet and 1,736 feet for the B-29. But what the Tornado lacked in size, it made up for in speed. It enjoyed a speed advantage over the wartime B-29 of more than 200 mph (cruising speed of 456 versus 230 mph, maximum speed of 579 versus 358 mph). The all-jet Boeing B-47, which first flew on December 17, 1947, made the contrast even greater. It weighed 206,700 pounds and cruised at 557 mph.

The same can be said about the first jet transports. The gross weight of the first commercial jet airliner, Britain's troubled de Havilland D.H. 106 Comet 1, which began operations in 1952, was only 107,000 pounds. This made the Comet somewhat lighter than the propeller-driven Lockheed L.1049A Super Constellation (120,000 pounds) and the same size as the Douglas DC-6B (107,000 pounds), with which it competed. With a very low takeoff thrust-to-weight ratio, the Comet was capable of carrying 44 passengers a distance of no more than 1,750 miles. The L.1049C Super Constellation, in comparison, could carry 88 passengers hundreds of miles farther, nonstop the entire 2,450 miles from Los Angeles to New York. Like the B-45 Tornado, what favored the Comet was its higher speed and cruising altitude. The sleek British jet flew at 490 mph at 35,000 feet, where the air is smoother and thinner, while the Super Constellation cruised at only 280 mph at 23,000 feet, where passengers complained about a rough ride and noise. Unfortunately, the pressurized fuselage of the Comet in which the passengers sat was prone to catastrophic metal fatigue. In 1954, after three of the airplanes disintegrated in flight, the Comet had to be withdrawn from service until it could be completely reengineered.

The B-52 Design Evolution

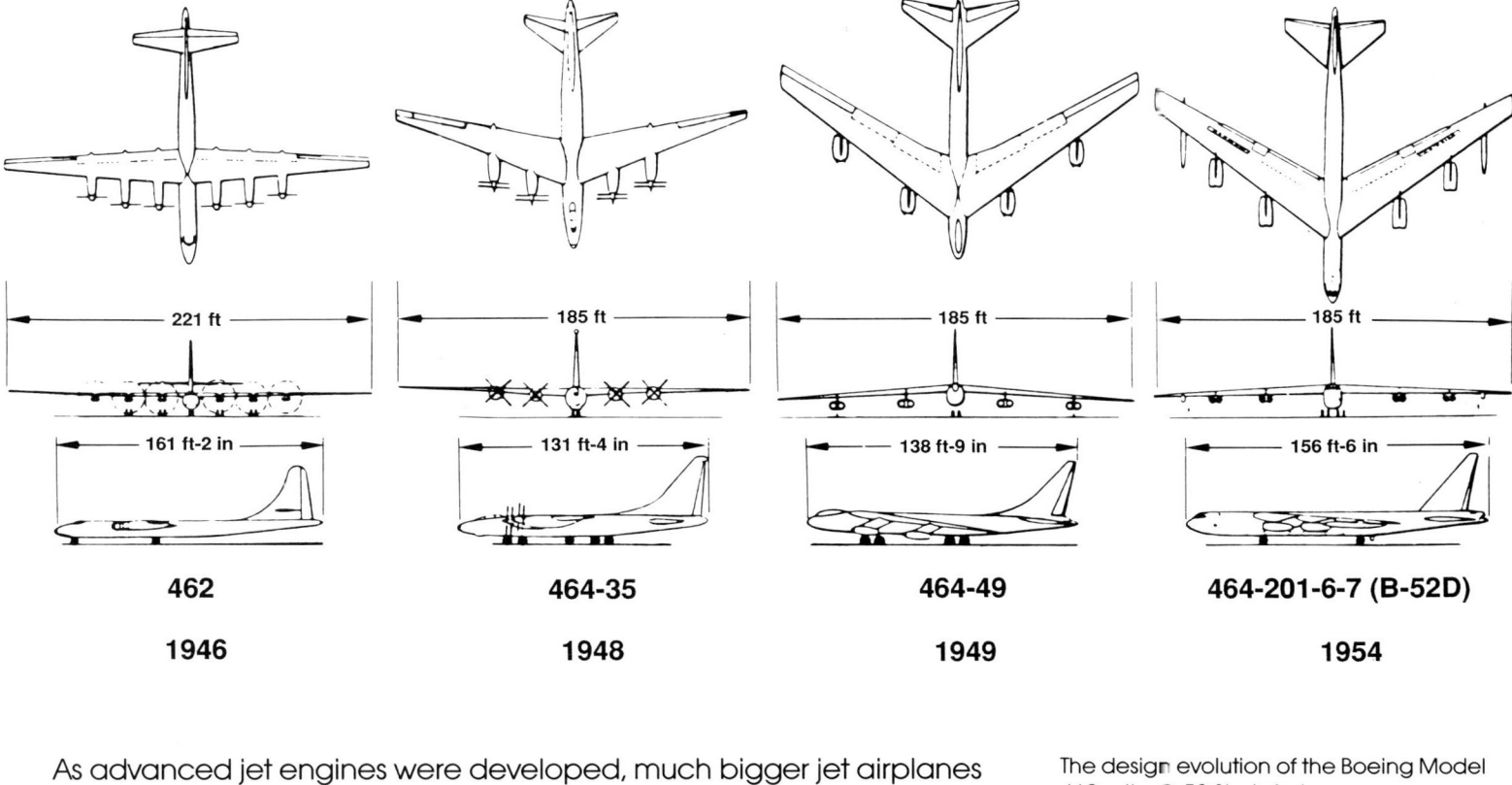

221 ft	185 ft	185 ft	185 ft
161 ft-2 in	131 ft-4 in	138 ft-9 in	156 ft-6 in
462	**464-35**	**464-49**	**464-201-6-7 (B-52D)**
1946	**1948**	**1949**	**1954**

As advanced jet engines were developed, much bigger jet airplanes came along, especially for military operations. In the United States, the first remarkably big jet was the Boeing B-52 Stratofortress. The intercontinental jet bomber had taken 10 years to develop and had required a number of major critical design changes, including the ability to be refueled in the air. The new Boeing bomber went from a straight-wing with six turboprop engines, through a 20-degree swept-wing with turboprops, to a 35-degree sweep with eight Pratt & Whitney J 57 turbojets, each engine capable of delivering more than 10,000 pounds of thrust. The XB-52 flew in April 1952 and production B-52s entered operational squadron service with the SAC in June 1955. In May 1956, a B-52 dropped the first airborne hydrogen bomb over Bikini Atoll in the Pacific. By 1962, over 600 B-52s had been assigned to active SAC heavy bomber squadrons around the world and had come to form the

The design evolution of the Boeing Model 462—the B-52 Stratofortress.

Facing page (top):
A B-47E uses rocket-assisted takeoff to clear the runway faster and with a heavier gross weight.

Facing page (bottom):
The prototype of the de Havilland D.H.106 Comet I first flew in 1949. The Comet entered service with BOAC in 1952 but was withdrawn in 1954 after three catastrophic in-flight disintegrations.

With the 488,000-pound Boeing B-52, designers achieved stability in the size of the big bomber —no production bomber built since the Stratofortress has been larger. This B-52G from Fairchild Air Force Base, Washington, was photographed in 1977.

In the prototype Boeing XB-52, the pilot and copilot sat in a tandem arrangement similar to that of a B-47. In the production model, they sat side by side as in a commercial airliner. In both cases, their vantage point was over 20 feet above the runway.

Facing page (top):
This B-52 carries loads of air-launched cruise missiles (ALCMs) on pylons beneath the wings.

Facing page (bottom):
A low-angle view of a B-52G taking off from a Strategic Air Command base. The SAC runway is not only longer than a standard civilian runway, it is also about twice as wide.

backbone of the American strategic deterrent force. The Stratofortress remains in service with the Air Force as both a strategic bomber and a long-range reconnaissance aircraft.

No matter what measure is used, the B-52 was an extraordinarily big plane; no larger bomber has ever been built. Compared with the earlier B-47 Stratojet, which had been the largest American jet, the wing dimensions of the B-52 were enormous. The span extended out to 185 feet in comparison to the B-47's 116 feet, and the total area enveloped 4,000 square feet against the B-47's 1,428. But again, it was the weight of the airplane that best measured its size.

With a gross weight of 488,000 pounds, the later-model B-52s far exceeded the size of any airplane that had come before them except for Geddes's hypothetical airliner. Even the Hughes H-4 Hercules fell short of the B-52's gross weight by 88,000 pounds. The B-52 appeared in seven different model configurations (B through H), all of which were heavily modified with new avionics, standoff missiles (short-range attack missiles [SRAMs], air-launched cruise missiles [ALCMs], and decoys), conventional ordnance delivery racks, wing and body skin, and so much more that there is more than a little truth in the observation that today's B-52Gs and B-52Hs contain nothing of the original production-line models. Moreover, it was precisely the B-52's "growth" capability that has made it such a great and durable aircraft.

COMMERCIAL JETLINERS

The Boeing 707 has seen extensive service around the world since its appearance in the late 1950s.

A basic reason why a bomber has to be so big, in comparison to an airliner, is that a bomber has to fly round-trip nonstop. This means that, pound for pound, the bomber has to carry more fuel. Another basic reason is economics. While military requirements had often stimulated the development of very large airplanes, the stringent economics and required efficiencies of commercial aviation have always affected the size of passenger transports. Clearly, it made no sense to be flying big airplanes that were half filled, while smaller, more efficient aircraft could be operated more often and more profitably along the same routes.

Size did not become the focus of progress in transport aircraft design until the phenomenal increase in the total number of revenue passenger miles (RPMs in airliner terminology), airline economics, growing congestion of the airways, and improved technology prompted that change in the late 1960s. In 1949, the total number of RPMs flown by American carriers on all domestic and international flights together stood at 8.8 billion. By 1959, it had risen markedly to 32.5 billion. In the following 10 years, however, that number shot meteorically to 136.1 billion. By 1986, it had more than doubled again, to about 350 billion RPMs, as new markets were exploited.

Underlying these statistics was the revolution in air transportation that came with the refinement and widespread adoption of the jet airliner, more powerful and efficient high bypass turbofan engines with significantly lower specific fuel consumption, and the growing desire of tourists to spend more time at their vacation spots and less time getting to them. The only problem the airlines and the aircraft manufacturers had to solve was the pleasant one of how to serve the snowballing needs of the flying public more profitably.

Their answer in the late 1960s, specifically for nonstop cross-country, coast-to-coast, and transoceanic operations, was that "bigger is better." They created a new category of airplane, the jumbo jet, that represented a new generation of jet transports with wide-body fuselages up to 255.5 inches in diameter, sophisticated wings with high-lift devices, large passenger-carrying capacities, and much more powerful and efficient high-bypass-ratio turbofan engines. Among the preceding jetliners were a number of highly successful and profitable medium- and long-range, high-passenger-capacity aircraft on whose engineering and operational experience much of the jumbo jet's design would be built.

As de Havilland introduced, and then withdrew, its Comet 1 in the early 1950s, Boeing was building its Model 367-80 (Dash 80) prototype of what became the 707, its first commercial jetliner. In the Dash 80, Boeing adopted the successful design pattern of a swept-back wing and pylon-mounted underwing engines that it had established with the B-47 and B-52 bombers and with the Model 717 jet tanker prototype (KC-135). When the Boeing 707 entered airline service with Pan Am in 1958, it set the pattern for early jet transports. Primarily a long-haul aircraft that was most efficient on trans-continental (707-120 series) and international (707-320 series) routes, the 707 had less powerful and fuel efficient turbojet engines, which made it profitable on long flights but restricted its use to airports with runways over 10,000 feet long.

Boeing has built 917 aircraft in the 707 line, excluding military versions, which it is still producing (seven are planned for 1989), making it the most successful airplane of the early jetliners, and one of the most successful transports ever produced. In 1989, 219 Boeing 707s were still in use around the world, although none are now flown by scheduled airlines in the United States. At 257,000 pounds, the 707-120—series aircraft weighed more than twice as much as the pioneering de Havilland Comet, and was far more

In the late 1950s and early 1960s, the Douglas DC-8 seriously challenged the Boeing 707 for primacy in the commercial jet airliner market. Although an excellent aircraft, the DC-8 entered airline service in 1959, a year after the Boeing 707, which hampered its sales. United Air Lines put its first DC-8-11s into service between San Francisco and New York in September 1959.

The Douglas DC-8 Super 62.

productive, despite its operational limitations. Configured for high-density seating, the early 707-series aircraft was capable of carrying up to 179 passengers (147 seats standard) at speeds up to 600 mph over a nonstop distance of 3,000 miles.

Another successful early commercial jet transport, and competitor of the 707s, was the Douglas DC-8 series (556 built through 1972). At 273,000 pounds, it weighed slightly more than the 707 and could carry 179 passengers a nonstop distance of over 5,000 miles. In respect to aircraft size, however, the DC-8's life history is more interesting for what it shows about the possibilities of making an airplane bigger by stretching it.

The purpose of *stretching* is to create an airplane with greater passenger capacity without going to the time and expense of designing an entirely new structure. When stretching an airplane, all the manufacturer usually has to do is put a couple of "barrel sections" or "plugs" into the existing fuselage. Sometimes it has to do little more, except for some collateral redesigning of the tail surfaces and landing gear and perhaps adding some wing area and new engines for more power, none of which requires any major retooling of production facilities. The airplane is already designed. The cockpit, the wing (or at least a wing that can be modified), and the engines already exist. The financial and engineering advantages of this "cut and stitch" approach to making a larger airplane should be apparent.

In the mid-1960s, McDonnell Douglas stretched the fuselage of its DC-8 in order to add seats that would make the aircraft more attractive to the airlines and more competitive with Boeing's larger 707-320B/C models. Twenty-foot barrel sections were added ahead of and behind the airplane's

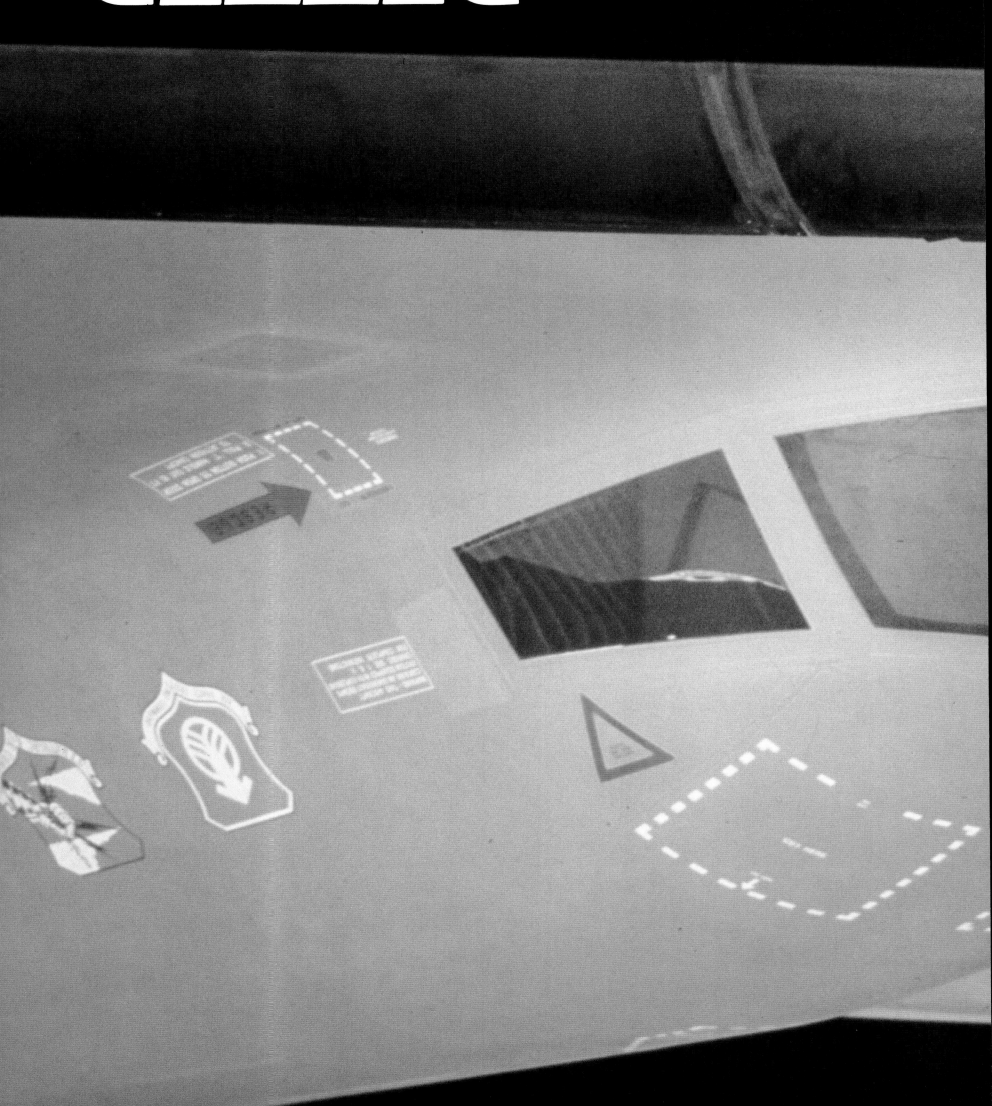

BETTER
The Quest for Excellence

RICHARD K. SMITH

At Hunaudières racetrack in August 1908, Wilbur Wright publicly demonstrcted the new two-seat Wright Model A.

Pages 222–223:
The exterior of the cockpit area of the Stealth bomber.

In the half century between 1903 and 1953, well within the life span of a single generation, human ingenuity transformed a fragile, clumsy, and unreliable vehicle of no practical utility into a magic carpet that routinely served global transportation. It is a tale of engineers, mechanics, and artisans, and their cumulative labors to master the mechanics of flight, extracting dramatic measures of energy from a minimum of material, and manipulating structures to maximize the machine's productivity. Science did not have much to do with it. Indeed, the airplane did more for science than science ever did for the airplane.

Although it is customary to date the beginning of mechanical flight at December 17, 1903, when the Wright brothers made their powered flight at Kitty Hawk, the curtain raiser, in fact, occurred on August 8, 1908. On that day, at Hunaudières racetrack near Le Mans, France, Wilbur Wright demonstrated to a startled world that the airplane could be controlled and flown. This was modern aviation's starting point.

The Weight Envelope: Weight, Power, and Payload

In the dawn of mechanical flight, the airplane was of necessity a fragile machine of sticks and wire. The small power then available in internal combustion engines, and their poor ratio of power to thrust, dictated this. Although the Wrights and many of the pioneers of flight often built their own, engines were ordinarily a "shelf" item provided by an outside supplier whose bread-and-butter in 1908 was typically engines for automobiles, in which engine weight was not critical to performance. The manufacture of aero engines quickly became a specialty unto itself, and was disciplined toward designing for maximum power from a minimum of material. After selecting an engine with the best power-to-weight ratio, the only area in which an airplane designer could save weight was in the airplane's structure.

In no other machine is weight as critical as it is in the airplane. Francis R. Shanley (1904–1969), a legendary professor of aerostructures at the University of California, Berkeley, liked to puzzle his classes with the question: "In an airplane structure, do we wish to aim in the direction of infinite strength, or in the direction of zero weight?"

Shanley gave his students a few minutes in which to mull this over.

224

Factory, U.S.A., and Clark series of airfoils, among many others. They constituted a hodgepodge of data. NACA spent some 10 years analyzing these and other airfoils in the VDT, standardizing their information and rationalizing them in terms of "NACA numbers." In 1933 the first results of these data were published, creating a worldwide sensation among aerodynamicists. These and subsequent results created a continuous "mail-order catalogue" of airfoils. No longer did an airplane designer have to hunt and scrape through dozens of obscure publications for the airfoil properties he sought, reworking their data to determine what was desired. The growing catalogue of NACA information had it all, and the properties of available airfoils were reduced to a shelf item.

NACA also built a wind tunnel for testing propellers. Twenty feet in diameter, it was used primarily to study the relationship between propeller flow and the fuselage or wing, but the Propeller Research Tunnel (PRT) served many other purposes. Put into operation in July 1927, the most significant products of the PRT were: (1) quantifying the aerodynamic drag of protuberances such as struts, wires, engines, and fixed landing gear; (2) developing the NACA cowling for the air-cooled radial engine; and (3) determining the installation of a wing-mounted engine relative to propeller flow in the vicinity of the wing. These data constituted further shelf information, and they served to fix a generalized shape for the airplane.

Everyone knew that fixed landing gear created substantial aerodynamic drag, but no one knew exactly how much. In 1928 NACA engineers put a

In 1928, using the new propeller research wind tunnel at Langley Laboratory, Virginia, NACA engineers developed and validated the deep chord engine cowling to improve the streamlining of the airplane and the cooling of the radial air-cooled engine. It was among the most significant aviation developments of the interwar years.

241

The exposed cylinder heads of this air-cooled Pratt & Whitney Wasp radial engine used in a Boeing P-12 pursuit airplane of the U.S. Army Air Corps were great sources of aerodynamic drag in aircraft of the 1920s. Much of NACA's research effort was directed toward solving this problem.

cluttered Sperry Messenger biplane with its landing gear removed in the PRT, and then informed the world that landing gear meant a breathtaking 40 percent of an airplane's drag. The exposed cylinders of an air-cooled engine contributed another 17 percent.

Having quantified a landing gear's drag, NACA could leave its correction to the industry. The drag of the air-cooled engine was different: It was not enough to throw a streamlined shroud around it; provision also had to be made for adequate airflow to cool the engine. The NACA method consisted of two cowlings, an aesthetically pleasing wrapper that greets the eye and an unseen inner cowling that controls the airflow within the enclosure. Carefully designed baffles were placed between and behind the engine's cylinders to further control airflow. This was a crude beginning of what some 20 years later would be called internal aerodynamics. The cowling not only added to the airplane's streamlined form, it made for more uniform heat exchange, permitting the engine to run at somewhat higher and more efficient temperatures.

In most single-engine airplanes powered by radial engines, the NACA cowling contributed to at least a 10-mph increase in speed. However, its results on multiengine airplanes were generally disappointing. This inspired the study of propeller and nacelle effects relative to airflow across the wing. Dozens of engine locations relative to the wing were examined, the most practicable proving to be in the wing's leading edge with the propeller a substantial distance ahead of the wing. Boeing soon used this data to design the engine locations for its B-9 bomber and then the 247 airliner of the early 1930s. The Glenn Martin Company used a similar engine placement for its B-10, but added the NACA cowlings, an enclosed cockpit, and fully retractable landing gear to push the plane's speed to 200 mph and win an

Air Corps production contract over the B-9. Engine location research in the 1930s fixed the shape of most multiengine propeller-driven airplanes from that time to our own.

Jimmy Doolittle stands next to a Lockheed Vega 5A Executive, owned by Shell Oil Company from 1930 to 1934, that he used in a number of speed and distance races. The streamlined NACA cowling over the engine reduced its aerodynamic drag and increased its speed significantly.

The Aircraft Designer

Although the designing of airplanes occasionally draws on the stuff of theoretical science, it ordinarily depends on the techniques of engineering, which consist more of perspicacity, perspiration, and imagination than of inspiration. This work of NACA consisted of running the same tests again and again—each time under new circumstances—measuring the results, and working up comparative analyses of the data. This has come to be known as *parameter variation*, but engineers call it "cut-and-try." Airplane design is of necessity scientific, but it has less to do with pure "science" than it has with art—the art of the engineer.

Nevil Shute, best remembered for the novels he wrote for his personal entertainment, was an aeronautical engineer by profession. With pencil, paper, and slide rule, he designed airplanes and later managed their manufacture. Indeed, in 1931 he managed the production of the Airspeed Courier, the first British biplane with retractable landing gear. In his novel *No Highway* (1947) Shute summed up airplane design with the remark: "A beautiful aircraft is the expression of the genius of a great engineer who is also a great artist."

Instead of a palette of colors, the aeronautical engineer has his own artist's palette of options. How he mixes these engineering options on his technological palette and applies them to his canvas (design) determines the performance of his airplane. When the synthesis is best it yields synergism, a result that is dramatically greater than the sum of its parts. This is hailed as "innovation." Failing this, there will result a mediocre airplane that may be good enough, or perhaps an airplane of lovely external appearance, but otherwise an iron peacock that everyone wants to forget.

Better Engines, Better Propellers

At the end of World War I, the horsepower available in an aero engine was typically 300. In 1926 it crossed the 500 mark; the 1,000 point was reached in 1933; by 1939 1,500 horsepower was on the shelf and 2,000 was becoming available. Of itself this would mean little without the engine's power-to-weight ratio also improving. The 9-cylinder 160-horsepower Gnome R-970 engine that powered a Sopwith Camel fighter of 1918 had a power-to-weight ratio of 1:2.4; the 14-cylinder 2,000-horsepower Pratt & Whitney R-2800 Double Wasp of 1940 had a ratio of 1:1.2.

An engine is only half an airplane's thrust system; the other half is the unglamorous propeller. The engine generates power; the propeller transforms power to thrust. A propeller blade is simply an airfoil rotating around a fixed point, but instead of generating lift it generates thrust. The blades' angle of attack, or pitch, relative to the flight axis, determines the thrust's characteristics. During takeoff or climb, a low pitch delivers the most efficient thrust; in cruising, high pitch provides maximum thrust. This is similar to shifting gears in an automobile. Prior to 1932 the typical propeller was of fixed pitch, imposing distinct limitations on airplane performance.

In the mid-1920s a successful hydraulically actuated controllable-pitch propeller was developed in England, meeting nothing but apathy or resistance from most British designers. However, until the early 1930s, the biplane prevailed in British aviation and a biplane's thicket of aerodynamic drag could not adequately demonstrate the propeller's versatility. Many arguments were also made against the propeller's weight, complexity, and cost.

It was the demands of the North American environment that, after 1932, finally pushed the controllable-pitch propeller into common use. The less dense air of mile-high airports among the Rocky Mountains, combined with ever higher wing loadings among American airline equipment, forced the airlines to seek something that would improve takeoff and climb performance. The controllable-pitch propeller from Hamilton Standard was the answer.

Duralumin in Structural Development

In 1927 two events did great things for the airplane: durable aluminum alloy was confirmed as the best material for aircraft structures and the Lockheed Vega appeared. A year earlier NACA initiated an annual conference with designers from the aircraft industry. Given the isolation of NACA's Langley Laboratory on the edge of a swamp in Tidewater, Virginia, this facilitated an intense cross-pollination between researchers and users of NACA's research product that would not have occurred otherwise. These annual conferences were eminently useful and fruitful events; nothing similar to them occurred in Europe. On May 24, at the 1927 conference, E. H. Dix, Jr., a metallurgist of the Aluminum Corporation of America (ALCOA), announced the validation of Alclad, a new technique for the protection of aluminum aircraft alloys. In the history of the airplane, this was a great milestone.

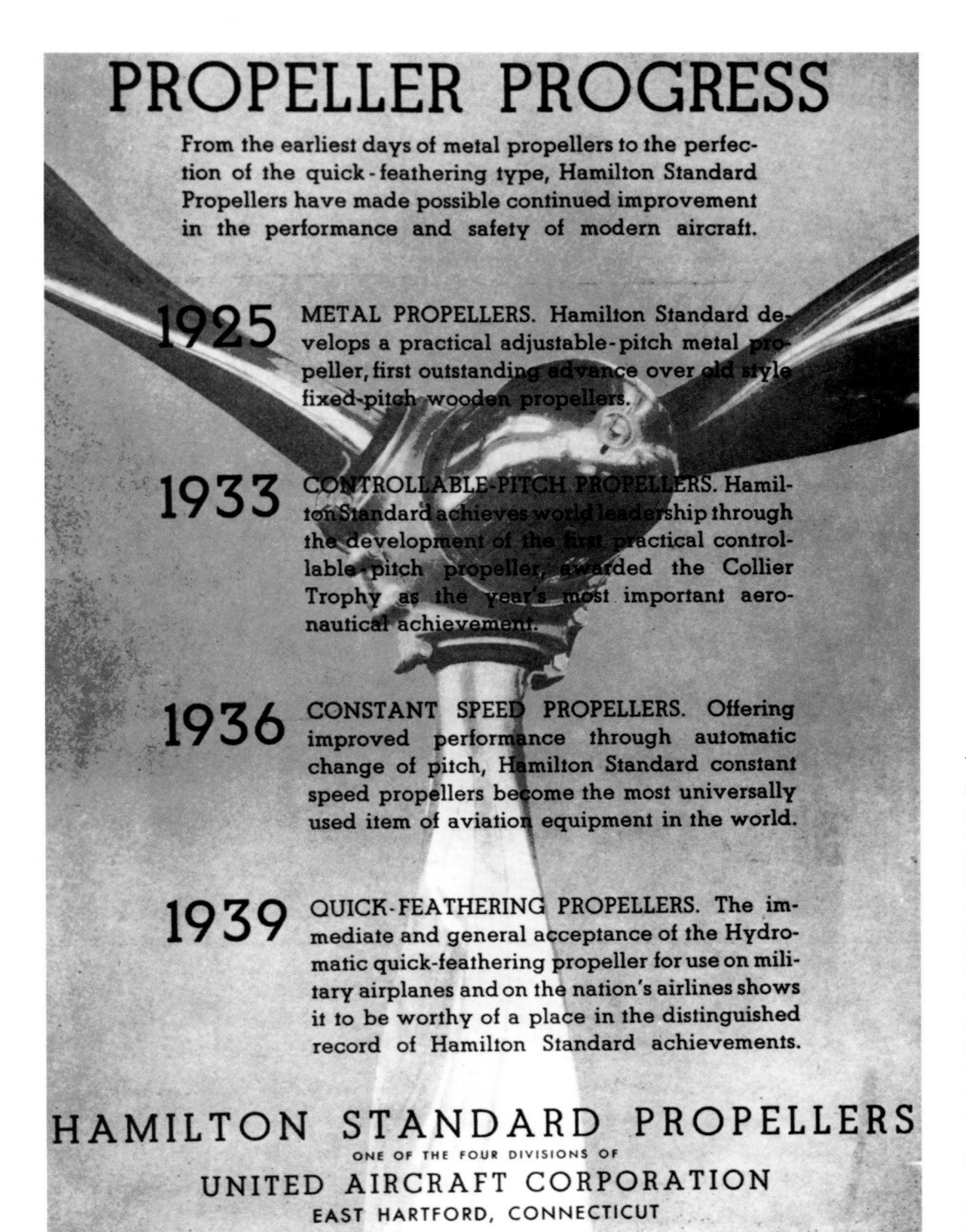

PROPELLER PROGRESS

From the earliest days of metal propellers to the perfection of the quick-feathering type, Hamilton Standard Propellers have made possible continued improvement in the performance and safety of modern aircraft.

1925 METAL PROPELLERS. Hamilton Standard develops a practical adjustable-pitch metal propeller, first outstanding advance over old style fixed-pitch wooden propellers.

1933 CONTROLLABLE-PITCH PROPELLERS. Hamilton Standard achieves world leadership through the development of the first practical controllable-pitch propeller, awarded the Collier Trophy as the year's most important aeronautical achievement.

1936 CONSTANT SPEED PROPELLERS. Offering improved performance through automatic change of pitch, Hamilton Standard constant speed propellers become the most universally used item of aviation equipment in the world.

1939 QUICK-FEATHERING PROPELLERS. The immediate and general acceptance of the Hydromatic quick-feathering propeller for use on military airplanes and on the nation's airlines shows it to be worthy of a place in the distinguished record of Hamilton Standard achievements.

HAMILTON STANDARD PROPELLERS
ONE OF THE FOUR DIVISIONS OF
UNITED AIRCRAFT CORPORATION
EAST HARTFORD, CONNECTICUT

The controllable-pitch propeller is a vital constituent of the modern airplane. Without it, the redesign of the aerostructure, streamlining, and all the other significant aspects of the modern airplane would have been impossible. The propeller constitutes one-half of the airplane's thrust system; it transforms the engine's power to thrust. The ability to vary propeller pitch gave designers control over the thrust delivered. Controllable pitch shortened the takeoff run, reduced the landing run and rollout, and increased engine efficiency at cruising speeds. In the 1930s, the principles of the Hamilton Standard hydraulic controllable-pitch propeller were licensed to manufacturers in Great Britain, Germany, France, Italy, and Japan. By the end of the 1930's, other manufacturers had developed techniques for propeller control that evaded the Hamilton Standard patents. Most notable was the Curtiss electrically actuated propeller.

This aluminum aircraft alloy is duralumin. (Pronounced "d'*ral*-uh-mun," in the industry it is usually called dural, pronounced "d'ral.") It was discovered in September 1906 by Alfred Wilm, a German chemist employed by an agency of the Prussian War Ministry, who was in quest of a lightweight metal to supplant brass in cartridge casings. In one experiment, Wilm alloyed pure aluminum with 3.5 percent copper, 0.5 percent manganese, and 0.5 percent magnesium. Wilm's laboratory assistant started testing the material on a Saturday, but at noon he quit for the day, accidently permitting the alloy to "age" over the weekend. When testing resumed on Monday, it was discovered that the material's strength had multiplied by a factor of five. This seemed incredible, but the experiment proved to be repeatable. The material was not acceptable for cartridge casings, but Wilm knew he had something good and he patented it.

In 1908 Wilm quit the government agency and licensed his patent to the Dürenmetallwerke A.G. of Düren. The company marketed the alloy under the name Düraluminium. The alloy's primary application to aeronautics was in the structures of Zeppelin airships. Among the multiple redundancies of a

Zeppelin's lightly loaded structure, Düraluminium performed well, but it eventually became apparent that it was flawed. Exposed to the atmosphere, the alloy was susceptible to intercrystalline embrittlement, sometimes called exfoliation, and generally known as corrosion.

Employed in an airplane's determinate structure, which is inevitably exposed to the atmosphere, Düraluminium's vulnerability posed an eventual hazard. This did not prevent Dr. Hugo Junkers, Claudius Dornier, and Adolf Rohrbach, the world's leaders in all-metal aerostructures, from using the material. They acknowledged the alloy as an experimental metal; it was important to learn from its applications. It is noteworthy that during World War I both Dornier and Rohrbach were employees of the Zeppelin Company; it was Zeppelin's use of Düraluminium that introduced these two men to the material and that propagated its use.

Shortly after World War I, at the Zeppelin factory at Staaken-Berlin, Rohrbach designed and built the Zeppelin Staaken E.4/20, a 4-engine 18-passenger airliner of 18,700 pounds and all-metal construction that flew in 1920. By the standards of 12 years later, many aspects of its external form were crude: the poor location of its engines and propellers relative to the

HUGO JUNKERS

Dr. Hugo Junkers (1859–1935) was 49 years old when Wilbur Wright flew at Hunaudières in 1908. He was already well known for his work on internal combustion engines and had made a fortune manufacturing small gas-operated hot water heaters for domestic use. For almost 20 years his name was synonymous with the all-metal airplane. The trademarks of Junkers were a low-wing monoplane configuration and a corrugated skin. In 1915 Junkers built his J-1, an all-metal airplane fabricated from sheet steel. It flew, but was too heavy to be a practical airplane; in 1916 Junkers switched to duralumin. Junkers's designs consisted of a duralumin framework covered by unstressed, duralumin corrugated sheeting. Although the corrugated skin inevitably made a contribution to stiffness, its primary function was simply to serve as an outer cover. In the 1920s and 1930s Junkers built a series of eminently successful airplanes—the F13, G23, G24, W33, Ju 52, Ju 86, and Ju 160—that became worldwide sales successes. Truly sensational was his four-engine G38 of 53,000 pounds, which some years after 1929 was the largest land plane in the world. After his finances became overextended, Junkers gradually lost control of his company, which became virtually nationalized under the Nazis. Hugo Junkers died near Munich on February 3, 1935, on his 76th birthday.

Hugo Junkers.

The Junkers G 31.

CLAUDIUS DORNIER

Claudius (often given as Claude) Dornier (1884–1969) designed and built bridges in Germany until 1910. He then became a structures engineer for Luftschiffbau Zeppelin, which was at that time the only firm in the world working with duralumin for aerostructures. During World War I Dornier was in charge of the Zeppelin works at Lindau, which developed large, all-metal flying boats. Because of the original limitations on German aviation in the Treaty of Versailles, after 1919 Dornier created companies in Italy and Switzerland in order to build his airplanes without restrictions. In the 1920s Dornier developed a family of commercial flying boats that culminated in the rugged and versatile twin-engine Wal. In 1929 he produced the Do X, a 12-engine flying boat that was the largest airplane in the world for almost a decade. The Do X was a white elephant, but a magnificent beast. During the early years of World War II, the Dornier company produced a series of twin-engine bomber and reconnaissance aircraft—Do 17s, Do 215s, and Do 217s—which were workhorses for the Luftwaffe. With the Allied victory in 1945, Dornier was put out of business, but his business gradually revived beginning in the mid-1950s. Dornier died in 1969 at the age of 85, but the company that bears his name continues to build airplanes.

Claudius (Claude) Dornier.

ADOLF ROHRBACH

Adolf Rohrbach (1889–1939) was born in Gotha, Germany. After graduating from engineering school, he took up naval architecture. When Luftschiffbau Zeppelin expanded into airplane design and manufacture during World War I, he became an engineer for the Zeppelin-Staaken works near Berlin. Here he developed an all-duralumin wing designed around a single box spar (the leading and trailing edges being cantilevered from it) and covered with duralumin sheeting carrying most of the structural loads. The four-engine E.4/20 airliner that Rohrbach built in 1920 is generally regarded as the prototype of the modern airliner. Under the terms of the Treaty of Versailles, it was seized and destroyed by the victorious Allies in 1922. When Allied controls on German aviation were relaxed after 1926, Rohrbach built a series of large, multiengine flying boats and airliners for Lufthansa. A scandal within the government relating to Germany's secret rearmament efforts of the late 1920s practically destroyed the company. In 1929 Rohrbach established an American company, but the effects of the Depression quickly consigned it to oblivion. Rohrbach failed to find a significant place for himself in Hitler's Germany in the 1930s; he died in Berlin in 1939.

Adolf Rohrbach.

The all-metal Rohrbach Roland II began service with Lufthansa in 1929.

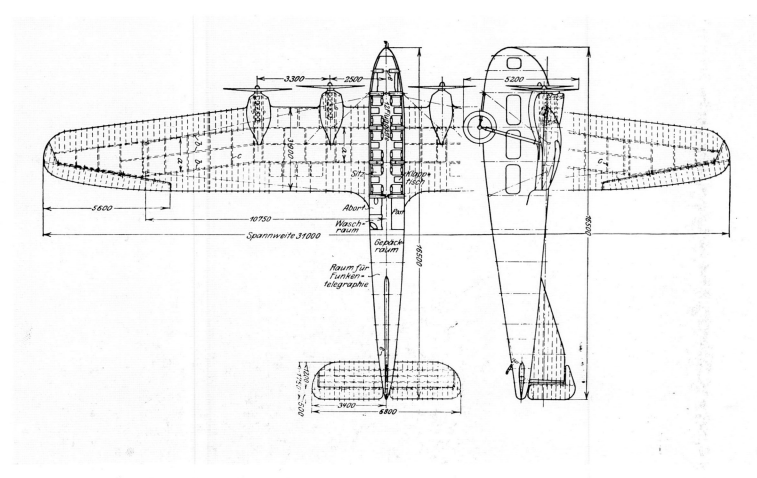

In terms of aerostructure, the Zeppelin-Staaken E.4/20 of 1919 was the great-grandfather of the modern airplane. Its gross weight of 18,740 pounds and wing area of 1,141 square feet produced a wing loading of 16.4 pounds per square foot, slightly higher than that of the Boeing 247 airliner produced 13 years later. Four 245-horsepower Maybach engines produced only 980 horsepower, less than that of the single Wright R-1820-G2 used in the early-model Douglas DC-3s. The E.4/20 cruised at 120 mph and carried 12 passengers.

wing surface, and a fixed landing gear that radiated extraordinary drag. By the standards of 1920, however, the E.4/20 looked like something from a science fiction story: a flying machine created by some extraterrestrial civilization.

Most unusual was the E.4/20's wing design. It consisted of a massive, full-span central box-section Düraluminium girder from which an all-metal leading edge and trailing edge were cantilevered; the whole was covered by stressed Düraluminium sheeting. The vertical and horizontal stabilizers employed similar cantilever construction. Wing loading was 16 pounds per square foot, unusually high for 1920. In terms of its elementary stressed-skin cantilever wing structure, the E.4/20 was the great grand-daddy of the "modern airplanes" of the 1930s.

Except for its use of metal, the E.4/20's fuselage was not unusual. It consisted of a conventional framework made of Düraluminium and covered by metal sheeting, the sheeting displacing the diagonal crosswires ordinarily used to give stiffness to a wooden structure. Clearly, in this "first cut" at such an extraordinary airplane, Rohrbach built as strongly as possible and the E.4/20 was a heavy machine. Its load-to-tare ratio of 28:72 was only a trifle better than the Wright brothers' airplane of 1904, and substantially less than the norm of 34:66. Nevertheless, the E.4/20 was an extraordinary airplane, and on this point deserves comparison with the Douglas DC-2 of 14 years later.

Unfortunately for Rohrbach, in 1920 Germany was a defeated nation. The victorious Allies were determined to keep Germany disarmed, and thus the Treaty of Versailles included crippling restrictions on the development of German military and civil aviation. In 1922 the Allies decreed that the E.4/20s had to be destroyed.

The British, French, and Americans experimented with Düraluminium, tinkering with its formula to improve its characteristics and to get around the Wilm patent. ALCOA sold it in the United States under the designation 17S. Its applications were made with great caution. Outside Germany it was

Cutting a door in the side of a Zeppelin-Staaken E 4/20 of 1919 would have created a large interruption in the hull structure, requiring reinforcements that would have increased the structural weight. Adolf Rohrbach got around this problem by having passengers enter at the front of the fuselage's "tube" through a door in the nose.

typically used in unstressed parts of the airplane—such as fuel tanks, fairings, seats, and instrument panels—but not in primary structures. Meanwhile, Düraluminium's spelling was simplified to the more pronounceable *duralumin*.

While high-strength duralumin is vulnerable to corrosion, pure aluminum develops an oxide that renders it impervious to corrosion. ALCOA developed a technique for cladding duralumin sheeting with microscopically thin coatings of pure aluminum that protected it from corrosion. In effect, the duralumin was sandwiched between pure aluminum coatings. The improved material was trademarked as Alclad, and this is what Dix announced at the NACA industrial conference of 1927. At the same time, in England, a technique was developed for anodizing duralumin. ALCOA's cladding was used on duralumin sheeting; anodizing was most effectively used on forgings and castings or pieces with irregular shapes. The protection given by cladding and anodizing served to establish a dramatically new baseline for aerostructures. After 1927 aluminum aircraft alloys became commonplace in aerostructures, and improved variants went from strength to greater strength.

The Lockheed Vega

Another critical event of 1927 was the appearance of the first of Lockheed's famous Star series, the Vega. A high-wing single-engine monoplane of 3,400 pounds designed for airline service, it seated six passengers. With an internally braced wing covered with stressed plywood and with a plywood stressed-skin fuselage, the Vega presented an extraordinarily well-streamlined form. The Vega's semi-monocoque fuselage was feasible only as a result of the Loughead brothers, Malcolm and Allan, and their chief engineer, John K. Northrop, developing a technique for manufacturing prefabricated fuselage shells that avoided the time-consuming handwork previously associated with that form of construction. The result was an airframe of light weight, great strength and stiffness, and unusual aerodynamic cleanliness.

The Vega prototype had a load-to-tare ratio of 45:55, and although this deteriorated to 40:60 in its final version, the Vega's useful load was increased

John K. Northrop, who later created Northrop Aviation, designed the Lockheed Vega. The plane's unusual performance resulted from its clean cantilever wing and unusual technique for manufacturing very light prefabricated wooden fuselage shells. Here Vega fuselage half shells are being readied in the fuselage room.

This early Lockheed Vega 5 (Lockheed serial number 23, NC 7953) was manufactured in December 1928 with a Pratt & Whitney Wasp engine but without a NACA cowling. Its maximum speed was 165 mph.

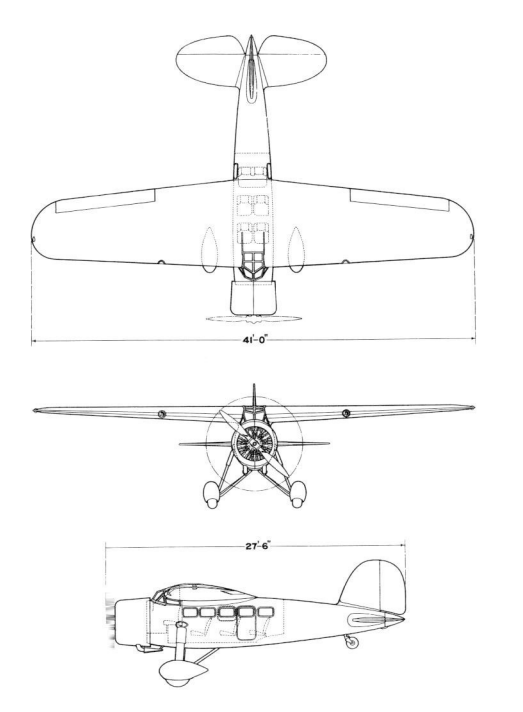

This three-view drawing clearly shows the clean lines that gave the Vega the lowest drag coefficient of any operational airplane in 1930. Lockheed's detailed multiview drawing provides a resumé of all the salient technical features of the various Vega models.

The Lockheed 5C Vega, a 4,750-pound airplane with seats for six passengers, was the fully refined version, with a NACA cowling and aerodynamic wheel pants fitted. It cruised at 160 mph with a top speed of 185 mph. From 1928 to 1931, it was the world's fastest airliner and pound for pound carried a greater payload than did any similar airplane. The Vega shown here belonged to the Standard Aircraft Company of Hackensack, New Jersey.

19 percent by doubling its horsepower and increasing its wing loading. The Vega's original wing loading was 12.6; the final variant's was 17, a 34 percent increase. In other words, Lockheed took the Vega through the same process that the Wright brothers had taken their airplanes during the years 1903—1909. This is a path that any airplane design experiences as its engineers develop it from good, to better, to its best.

　　The Vega was not only a good load carrier, it had speed. In a day when most airplanes cruised at 100 mph, the original Vega cruised at 115 mph and had a top speed of 135. Its final variant cruised at 160 mph and had a top speed of 185, with much of this increase due to the adoption of the NACA cowling.

From the Vega to Orion to DC-2

In 1927, the same year the Vega appeared, Charles Lindbergh startled the world by flying nonstop from New York to Paris, 3,600 miles, in 33.5 hours, averaging 107 mph. This was a magnificent achievement, but compared to the Lockheed Vega, Lindbergh's *Spirit of St. Louis* was a "yesterday's airplane."

　　When Lindbergh sought a new airplane in 1929, he went to Lockheed;

This Lockheed Orion (NC 12222, Lockheed serial number 180) "flies" today as a restored exhibit at the Swiss Transport Museum in Lucerne. It began as an experimental Altair DL-2A in September 1931 but was converted to an Orion 9C Special in June 1932. For the next six years, Jimmy Doolittle, Shell Aviction Corporation's aviation manager, piloted it around the country as the *Shellightning*. After it had gone through a number of other owners, the Swiss Transport Museum purchased it in 1976. It was restored and repainted with the markings of one of SwissAir's original Orions, CH-167 (Lockheed serial number 189).

the results were the Lockheed 8 Sirius, which was essentially a low-wing Vega, and, later, its twin the Lockheed 8 Altair, which was equipped with retractable landing gear. Out of the Sirius and Altair experience Lockheed developed the Orion; it was designed for high-speed airline service with seats for six passengers.

The Orion, which first flew in early 1931, was simply a low-wing Vega, but with a profound difference. The Orion had retractable landing gear. Whereas the Vega's maximum speed was 185 mph, the Orion cruised at 200, and its more numerous 9 and 9D models had a top speed of 226 mph. An Orion could run away from any fighter plane in the world—all of which were still biplanes replete with struts, wires, and fixed landing gear. Europeans assumed that the Orion's performance was grossly exaggerated until 1932 when Swissair put two into service between Zurich and Vienna. Relative to European airline equipment, their daily performances were mind-boggling and soon inspired the design of the British Airspeed AS.5 Courier and Ernst Heinkel's He 70 in Germany. The plywood Orion pioneered the shape of today's airplane, but not its materials.

After 1932 all the constituents suddenly came together in America. Boeing built the twin-engine B-9 bomber based on its two Monomails. In 1933 Martin produced the B-10 bomber for the Army Air Corps. The B-10 delivered a ton of bombs at 190 mph, after which it sped away at 225 mph; its speed made all existing fighter planes obsolete. Boeing delivered its 247 airliner to United Air Lines in 1933, and then Douglas built the DC-1 for Transcontinental and Western Airlines (TWA), which went into production as

The Heinkel He 70 Blitz, developed for Lufthansa in 1932 as a response to the Lockheed Orion, was a 7,630-pound airliner with seats for four passengers. Although it had a metal semi-monocoque fuselage, the He 70 had a wooden wing covered with stressed plywood. With a top speed of 220 mph and a cruising speed of 190 mph, the He 70 was the fastest airplane produced in Europe in 1932.

The Boeing 247, which first flew in February 1933 and soon entered service with United Air Lines, was the first modern airliner. A 13,000-pound airplane with seats for 10 passengers, it was the first airliner to reduce coast-to-coast travel time to 20 hours. A more advanced model, the 247D, had a top speed of 200 mph and cruised at 180. However, the 247 was soon eclipsed by the superior performance of the 18,500-pound Douglas DC-2. This Boeing 247, which Roscoe Turner and Clyde Pangborn flew to a third-place finish in the MacRobertson Air Race of 1934, is on permanent display in the National Air and Space Museum.

the DC-2 in 1934. In August 1934, TWA's DC-2 Sky Chief service from Newark to Los Angeles slashed American transcontinental transportation to 18 hours, including en route fuel stops only at Chicago, Kansas City, and Albuquerque.

The updated airplane coincidentally created a distinct division of labor between the design of military and civil aircraft. Before 1933 any airliner was readily converted to a bomber simply by adding bomb shackles and defensive armament. With aircraft such as the Heinkel He 111 and Junkers Ju 86 and Ju 90, European airline fleets were often regarded as convertible, *ad hoc* bombers. However, the streamlined airplane dictated internal bomb stowage, and because bombs necessitated substantially less space than a human payload, hereafter fuselage cross-section designs of bombers and airline equipment would move in opposite directions.

The Douglas DC-2, which first flew on May 11, 1934, and went into service with TWA shortly thereafter. It was a smashing commercial success, with more than 190 built.

The Junkers Ju 90B went into service with Lufthansa in 1938.

THE MARTIN B-10'S COMBAT AIRPLANE REVOLUTION

A B-10B of the 6th Bombardment Group from France Field, Canal Zone, Panama, cruises over the Caribbean in November 1937.

Three B-10s from the 7th Bombardment Group at Hamilton Field, California, fly formation on air mail route 18 (note the marking "A.M. 18" on the fuselage) in then—Lt. Col. Henry H. Arnold's Western Zone during early 1934, when the Army Air Corps was responsible for flying the mail.

The Boeing Model 299 four-engine bomber made its first appearance in July 1935. The aircraft crashed taking off from Wright Field, Ohio, while undergoing flight tests by the Army Air Corps. The Flying Fortress was the backbone of the American strategic bomber force against Germany from 1942 to 1945. By the time production finally ended, 12,731 Flying Fortresses had been built.

The Glenn L. Martin Company's Model 123, generally remembered as the U.S. Army Air Corps' B-10 bomber, first flew in February 1932, started rolling off production lines in late 1933, and by the end of 1936 had established a global revolution in bomber design.

Prior to the B-10, multiengine bombers were typically angular biplanes without retractable landing gear, and although they usually had a metal structure, it was covered with fabric. Their crews sat in open cockpits, and the bombload was carried externally. Their best speed might be as fast as 120 mph; cruising speed was 95 mph. Except for much-improved reliability, their performances were only marginally superior to the rickety and treacherous multiengine bombers of World War I.

The Martin B-10 was a sleek stress-skinned all-metal monoplane of 16,400 pounds with a load-to-tare ratio of 40:60. It had retractable landing gear, its crew sat in enclosed cockpits, and the bombload was carried internally behind streamlined doors. At a B-10's takeoff weight, two 775-horsepower R-1820 engines provided a power-to-weight ratio of 1:10.5; with almost half its fuel consumed and its bombs gone, this ratio improved to 1:8.6. In 1935 the best fighters among all air forces of the world were biplanes, improved variants of World War I fighters, and a best power-to-weight ratio among these combat planes was 1:7; their best speed was 190 mph, but a B-10 could rush in at 185 mph to strike its target with a ton of bombs and speed away at 210 mph. As of 1935 there was not a fighter plane in the world that could catch a Martin B-10.

Once this fact was established, its portents came as a terrible shock to the military establishments of the world. The Martin B-10 inspired a global revolution in bomber design, immediately yielding the Heinkel He 111 and Dornier DO 17, Germany's workhorse bombers of World War II; the Japanese Mitsubishi G3M-1 and Ki-21; the Soviet Tupolev SB-2; the French Bloch 131; and the British Handley Page Hampden and Bristol Blenheim. It also inspired Boeing to double the number of a bomber's power units from two to four in its Model 299, the prototype of the legendary B-17 Flying Fortress that first flew in 1935.

All of these modern bombers were into production or flying in prototype before the end of 1936. All were first-line equipment when World War II started in September 1939, and most of them soldiered on to the end of the war in 1945.

Most significantly, B-10 performance provoked a revolution in fighter design, finally forcing it to part from the biplane. With the knowledge that it would require more firepower to destroy a faster bomber of all-metal construction and in minimal time, the threat of B-10 performance initiated a heavying-up of fighter armament from two to four, from four to six, and then from six to eight guns, as well as a movement toward guns of larger caliber. Most immediately, Martin B-10 performance inspired the designs of the Messerschmitt Bf 109, the Hawker Hurricane, and the Supermarine Spitfire, the principal antagonists of the fateful Battle of Britain in 1940.

KLM's *Uiver* at Waalhaven Airport, Rotterdam, after winning the MacRobertson London-to-Melbourne Air Race in 1934. It placed first in the transport division; in the overall competition it placed second to a custom-built race plane.

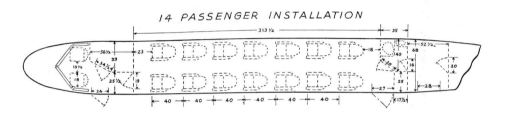

The cabin cross section and floor plan of the Douglas DC-2 were practically the same as those of the Ford and Fokker Tri-motors. However, the DC-2's cruising speed of 180 mph was 70 mph faster, and it required only two engines.

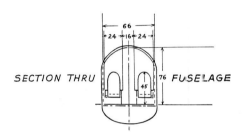

SECTION THRU FUSELAGE

14 PASSENGER INSTALLATION

The Lockheed 188 Electra four-engine, turbo-prop airliner was designed in the mid-1950s to meet an American Airlines requirement. The first Electra flew in 1957, and Eastern Air Lines and American initiated airline service with it in January 1959. In 1959—60, however, three Electras crashed and public confidence in the aircraft seriously eroded. The development of medium- and short-range jet airliners in the early and mid-1960s spelled the end for the Electra as a civilian airliner after production of 232 aircraft. The U.S. Navy, however developed the Electra into the extremely successful P-3 Orion land-based anti-submarine patrol aircraft. Through 1986, 611 Orions had been delivered to the U.S. Navy and a number of navies and air forces around the world.

The military airplane would take on many of the characteristics of a racehorse; a high-strung thoroughbred that was carefully stabled, exercised, and otherwise fussed over, to be ready for the bugle on race day. On the other hand, an airliner had to be a tough, reliable workhorse capable of earning its keep every day.

1934: The Year of Transition

In October 1934, the MacRobertson Race was flown, an intercontinental contest covering 11,300 miles between England and Australia. In England, the de Havilland Company developed its D.H.88 Comet racer expressly for this event. Three Comets were entered, and one won the race, but a Douglas DC-2 came in second and a Boeing 247 took third place. It was a terrible shock for British and European aircraft manufacturers to realize that these American airliners, designed to haul people through the sky efficiently, had matched the performance the of what was the world's finest long-distance racing plane.

The Sikorsky S-42, a four-engine flying boat of some 40,000 pounds, also took to the air in 1934, for Pan American Airways' South American service. Whereas a Boeing 247's wing loading was 15 pounds per square foot, and

One of Pan American Airways' 19-ton Sikorsky S-42 Clippers at the Pan American International Airport, Miami.

In November 1935, the Martin M-130 *China Clipper* inaugurated trans-Pacific air mail service from San Francisco to the Philippines via Hawaii and the islands of Midway, Wake, and Guam. Weighing 52,000-pounds, the M-130 was unusual in having a useful load of 23,500 pounds, 45 percent of its gross weight. The 2,410-mile San Francisco—Hawaii flight is the longest nonalternative over-water flight in the world, and an airplane that can fly it can continue to any other point in the world. The Martin M-130 was thus the first intercontinental airliner.

the DC-2's was 19.5, the S-42 was a startling 30. By making the structure carry more load, the S-42 achieved a load-to-tare ratio of 42:58. Ordinarily, such a high wing loading resulted in a high landing speed, but this was avoided in the S-42 by artful use of a large, trailing wing flap. The intense development and employment of wing flaps as auxiliary lift devices in the 1930s permitted airplane designers to exploit ever higher wing loadings.

Martin's M-130 also made its first flight in 1934. A flying boat of 52,000 pounds, the M-130 was intended to pioneer Pan American's trans-Atlantic service, but because of political problems the airline had to use it for trans-Pacific service. Among large airplanes the weight control achieved by the M-130's designers was extraordinary. As a bare airplane stripped of cabin furnishings, an M-130's load-to-tare ratio was 51:49, 44:56 with a fully equipped cabin.

In November 1935, Pan Am's M-130 *China Clipper* demonstrated its capabilities by inaugurating trans-Pacific air mail service. The 2,410 miles between California and Hawaii constitute the longest non-alternative over-water route between commercial destinations in the world. An airplane that can fly this distance can continue to any part of the world; it is an intercontinental vehicle. Although an M-130's payload over this distance was only some 2,600 pounds, no other airplane of these years could begin to equal it. The Martin M-130 was the world's first intercontinental airliner.

Having developed a streamlined shape that after 1934 became universal among new designs the world over, many small refinements became worthwhile: filleting junctions between wing and fuselage where minor air turbulence might occur; designing windows with frames that were flush with the exterior skin; insetting door handles and putting door hinges inside a door's opening; eliminating the thousands of tiny, drag-producing rivet heads by replacing them with countersunk, flush rivets; butting metal skin panels to eliminate the small discontinuities of airflow created by lapped skin junctions; and making tailwheels retractable.

Fred Weick, an NACA engineer working on his own, validated in 1934 the superiority of tricycle landing gear and a steerable nosewheel relative to the conventional tail-dragging configuration. Tricycle landing gear not only concluded the revolution in an airplane's ground handling initiated by the concrete runway and brakes, it also made vital improvements to takeoff and landing characteristics. Although a novelty in the 1930s, within a decade

The one and only Douglas DC-4E (E for Experimental) first flew on June 7, 1938. It was a 66,500-pound airplane with two-by-two seating for 42 passengers. The DC-4E was one of the first airplanes to have tricycle landing gear. Douglas would have preferred to have built the DC-4E with a single vertical stabilizer and rudder, but it would have been too tall to clear the lintel of hangar doors. The triple tail was dictated by the necessity of hangar door clearance. The American airlines finally decided that the DC-4E's performance was poor (cruising speed 200 mph), its systems were excessively complex and required too much maintenance, and its operating economics were unacceptable. Only one was built and used by United Air Lines for proving flights on its routes before being returned to Douglas, who sold it to Mitsui Trading Company in late 1939 for use by Greater Japan Air Lines. Although originally reported to have crashed in Tokyo Bay, the DC-4E was actually disassembled by the Nakajima Aircraft Company and became the basis for its four-engine long-range G5N Shinzan bombers used by the Japanese Navy. The Shinzan performed poorly, and only six were built. Douglas revised the DC-4E specification to a less complex aircraft that became the successful DC-4 (C-54) series.

A United Air Lines DC-3 over the northeast corner of New York's Central Park, demonstrating its ability to fly on one engine with the propeller of the other engine feathered. With a feathered propeller, the blades in the hub were rotated edgewise to the direction of flight. Without feathering, the dead propeller would continue to rotate in the wind, turning the dead engine and creating a great increase in aerodynamic drag.

American Airlines initiated the development of the Douglas Sleeper Transport (DST), a larger and faster version of the DC-2, in 1934. Two years later, the DST and the day transport versions of the DST fitted with Wright R-1820 engines, designated the DC-3, entered service with American Airlines and set the pattern for today's airliner service and reliability.

tricycle gear would be conventional, and the tail-dragger would be representative of the past. Until 1944 tricycle landing gear was also unique to American airplanes.

The year 1934 was the *annus mirabilis* of the airplane. The American aircraft industry gained a technological lead that the rest of the world did not catch up to until some 30 years later. The swift absorption and use of new foreign technologies, such as the turbojet engine, swept wing, and delta wing planform, only served to build on that lead in the years after World War II.

Increased Sophistication in Aircraft and Production

Until the 1930s the airplane was essentially a low-altitude machine. Although supercharging would support engines in the progressively thinner atmosphere above 10,000 feet, the problem was sustaining the human operator. Humans are comfortable enough up to altitudes of 10,000 feet (e.g., Mexico City is

THE C-46, THE C-47, AND THE LEGEND OF THE DC-3

The DC-3 legend is owed to this airplane being an extraordinarily well-designed flying machine, to its more than 13,000 productions, to the tens of thousands of aviators who flew it and loved it, and to the teething problems of the Curtiss CW-20.

However, it was the Douglas DC-1 that was a truly great airplane—a dramatic departure from the past. The DC-2, of which 193 were built, was the great demonstrator. The DC-3 is noteworthy for being the great economic vehicle. Although the 18,650-pound DC-2 had 75 percent more speed than the angular tri-motors it displaced, its cabin cross section measured only 66 inches. This was about the same as the old tri-motors, and it seated 14 passengers, seven on each side of the aisle. The 25,200-pound DC-3's cabin cross section measured 92 inches, permitting three-seat rows, 2 + 1 divided by the aisle, multiplying seating from 14 to 21.

For a 35-percent increase in gross weight, the DC-3 yielded a 50-percent increase in payload. The airlines were fond of saying that it was the first airliner with which they could make money by carrying passengers only. Assuming that they could fill a DC-3's 21 seats, an air mail subsidy was not necessary.

After the DC-3 first flew in 1935, the Curtiss-Wright Corporation initiated the design of a DC-3 replacement, its CW-20, which flew in March 1940. It weighed some 40,000 pounds, gigantic for a twin-engine airplane of this era. It had a pressure cabin that pioneered the "double-bubble" fuselage cross section. Its 118-inch cabin cross section accommodated 40 passengers in 2 + 2 seating and 50 passengers in 2 + 3 seating; the lower section of the double bubble had a generous capacity for cargo.

As a load carrier the CW-20 was not only superior to the DC-3, in 1940 it seemed clearly destined to replace it. However, Curtiss design staffs were notoriously conservative, and they sold short the CW-20's long-term future by designing it as a tail-dragger at the moment when tricycle landing had been validated. Needing a large-capacity troop carrier and cargo plane, the Army Air Forces rushed to order the CW-20 which it designated the C-46 Commando. Although the C-46's shell was designed to be pressurized, the Army never installed pressurization equipment.

The C-46 was a troubled airplane. It did not go into production until 1942. Rushed into service, the airplane had no body of test experience behind it and there were inevitably many resultant difficulties. Meanwhile, for want of a load carrier, the Army ordered DC-3s, designated C-47 in military service. Continued problems with the C-46 generated more stopgap orders for the C-47 and its variants. In lieu of the "best," the Army had to settle for "good enough"; the Navy adopted the DC-3, which became the R3D. By the end of the war, some 13,000 DC-3s and its military variants had been built; meanwhile only some 2,000 C-46s were produced.

Almost half a century after 1940 there are still a few hundred DC-3s in commercial operation, flying among the far pavillions of the world. Only a dozen or so CW-20s still exist, hauling freight around the Caribbean, but if it were not for the CW-20's teething problems, not nearly so many C-47s would have been produced and the legend of the DC-3 would not have achieved the magnificent dimensions it has.

The C-47.

The C-47.

The interior of the C-46.

The Curtiss Wright C-46 production line.

The C-47.

The C-46.

The Boeing 307 Stratoliner, a 42,000-pound airplane that seated 32 passengers, used the wing, engines, and tail group of the B-17 bomber. It was the first airliner with a pressure cabin, and its barrel-shaped fuselage permitted it to hurdle the Rocky Mountains at 20,000 feet. In coast-to-coast service from Los Angeles to New York, the 307 could fly the Los Angeles–Chicago leg nonstop.

7,600 feet above sea level), but above that altitude oxygen content falls off rapidly. Airliners such as the Douglas DC-3 did not fly over the Rockies; trying to stay below 10,000 feet, they flew between mountains, following valleys—and giving passengers a breathtaking view of mountains off each wingtip.

As early as 1930, Junkers in Germany and Farman in France demonstrated airplanes for high-altitude operations that had special pressurized chambers for their crews. In 1937 the U.S. Army Air Corps validated a pressure cabin in the Lockheed XC-35 that was inherently part of the airplane, its exterior skin serving as the pressure shell. Building on this technology, Boeing built its 307 Stratoliner as the world's first airliner with a pressure cabin. When Boeing went into transcontinental service with TWA in 1940, for the first time the North American continental divide could be routinely overflown at cruising altitudes in excess of 15,000 feet.

By the eve of World War II, all the basic constituents of the modern airplane were on the shelf for the use of airplane designers. In the course of the 1930s the airplane became an increasingly complex machine. Only nine months were required to design, build, and fly the Douglas DC-1 (September 20, 1932–July 1, 1933); in May 1934, just 22 months after the DC-1 contract award, production models of the 19,000-pound DC-2 were being delivered to TWA. However, three years were required to move the four-engine 73,000-pound Douglas DC-4 from preliminary design in 1939 to its first flight in February 1942. During this period, the entire industry expanded. In 1933 only some 7,800 persons were directly involved in the design and

manufacture of airplanes in the United States, whereas by 1939 the beginning of major prewar military expansion had pushed this number to more than 48,000.

By the end of the 1930s, manufacturers had organized the necessary divisions of labor among design teams into specialized groups: aerodynamics, structures, power plant, landing gear, various "systems," and armament, among others. Each had its piece of the airplane. Over them all, like a grim policeman, hovered the "weights group," which was always ready to invoke its First Commandment: Simplify and add a bit of lightness. Each area became a vital specialty, and after 1940 an engineer might devote a career of 30 years to designing landing gear, an absolutely unforgiving part of the airplane whose design was a demanding art unto itself.

Profiting from its experience with the DC-4E, Douglas Aircraft designed a completely new four-engine aircraft, the DC-4, that could accommodate 40 passengers. The outbreak of war with Japan prompted the U.S. government to take over DC-4 production. The Army Air Forces designated the new aircraft the C-54 Skymaster, which was heavily used in the Air Transport Command throughout the world. After the war, many wartime C-54s were converted to civilian use and additional DC-4s were built to serve the postwar needs of airlines worldwide.

World War II

Like the World War of 1914–1918, the Second World War was a period more noteworthy for production—expanding aviation's industrial base—and a determined exploitation of available technology than for unusual contributions to airplane design. Once again, war did more for aviation than it did for the airplane. In the United States alone, factory floor space increased from 9,455,000 square feet in 1939 to 168,000,000 square feet in 1945; the labor force rose from 77,500 persons in 1940 to a peak of 1.3 million in late 1943.

The Douglas DC-6B was one of the most successful airliners of the 1950s.

At first the obvious was suspected: a bomb placed aboard the airplanes. Another theory centered on turbine disintegration, the engine parts being hurled into the fuselage, destroying the pressurized cabin. However, corpses recovered from the sea showed no residue from explosives nor fragmentation injuries, but their condition bore clear evidence of explosive decompression of the cabin shell. Meanwhile, in April 1954, all Comets were grounded.

The possibility of metal fatigue seemed far-fetched; as yet, no Comet had been flown 4,000 hours, and even at 10,000 hours an airplane is still "new." However, the Comet was operating in a wholly new realm of flight. Although airplanes had been flying with pressure cabins since 1940, the cruising altitude of these propeller-driven machines rarely exceeded 25,000 feet. A Comet cruised at 35,000 feet.

Atmospheric pressure at sea level is 14.7 pounds per square inch, but at an altitude of 5,280 feet (the elevation of Denver, Colorado) it falls to 12.3; at 18,000 feet to 7.2; and at 35,000 feet to 3.3. An airplane's pressure cabin never attempts to create a sea-level environment. To do so would result in a significantly heavier and less efficient airplane, and it would serve no useful purpose.

Pressure cabins typically simulate an altitude of 8,000 feet. This results in 4.16 pounds per square inch on the cabin shell interior at 20,000 feet; 5.46 at 25,000 feet; 7.5 at 35,000 feet; and 8.0 at 40,000 feet. Equally important is the pressurization cycle, the number of times the cabin shell is pressurized and depressurized. With each cycle the cabin's structure expands and contracts, inflicting wear on its materials. In a service between London and Johannesburg a Comet flew through six cycles. The minimal maintenance

This Aloha Airlines Boeing 737 lost part of its fuselage skin over the Hawaiian Islands in April 1988.

The malfunctioning of a cargo door latch on this Boeing 747 resulted in the loss of a large section of the fuselage skin in February 1989.

required by a gas turbine gave the Comets a much higher utilization rate than piston-engine equipment, and their high cruising speed acted to put them through more pressurization cycles per hundred hours than a piston-engine airplane. Routine wear was accelerated.

In an epic salvage operation, the Royal Navy recovered 70 percent of one Comet's wreckage from the ocean floor. Concurrently, the Royal Aircraft Establishment acquired a Comet, built a tank around its fuselage, filled both with water to contain a possible explosion, and subjected the cabin shell to an accelerated cycling of pressurizations. After 3,057 cycles the test-tank Comet's fuselage failed. In terms of six cycles a day, 300 days a year, this amounted to 19 months of actual operation.

A comparison of this controlled test-tank failure and the wreckage brought up from the ocean floor showed striking similarities between the two cabin failures. Once the cabin experienced local failure, it immediately propagated itself throughout the structure. In flight, the airplane would be shredded within seconds. This was the inspiration for rip-stop construction: frequently occurring strongpoints designed into the cabin framing and shell that prevented a local failure from becoming catastrophic.

A dramatic demonstration of the effectiveness of rip-stop construction occurred in April 1988, when an aging Boeing 737 of Aloha Airlines started shredding its skin at 25,000 feet above the Hawaiian islands. Although the loss of cabin shell had mind-boggling dimensions, the airplane retained its structural integrity and the pilot was able to fly it to a safe landing.

In late February 1989, a Boeing 747 departing Honolulu for New Zealand lost a lower forward cargo door due to a lock failure. This caused a rapid decompression and the loss of a 10- by 20-foot section of the forward cabin and the power in two engines. Nine passengers were swept to their deaths. As with the Aloha Airlines 737, the aircraft retained its structural integrity, and the pilot was able to maneuver the plane back to the airport.

The Boeing 707

Although British gas turbine technology remained a world leader, as a result of the Comet's flawed design, Great Britain lost its lead in jet airliners. Totally redesigned, the Comet did not reenter airline service until late 1958. Meanwhile, Boeing came on the scene with its 707. Initially a design that not only spawned a formidable series of Boeing products, it established a label for an entire generation of airline equipment. Regardless of nationality or manufacture, the expression "707 Generation" describes all subsonic turbojet airline equipment weighing less than 500,000 pounds and built since 1955.

One aspect of the 707's technology transfer occurred in the early 1960s. After customer airlines have flown their airliners away from the factory, major manufacturers continue to keep track of their airplanes; the feedback from operations is vitally important for tomorrow's product. Boeing soon became aware that a 707-320 sold to Air France had "disappeared." The airplane was not operating, had not been destroyed in an accident, and could not be found anywhere. Inquiries to Air France elicited evasive replies. A year later this 707 suddenly reappeared in airline service. Perplexed, Boeing inaugurated its own investigation. Eventually, it was determined that this airplane had been flown to Toulouse, a center of aircraft manufacturing in the south of France, where it had been totally dismantled and its components subjected to detailed study.

There is nothing reprehensible about such dismantling. Given the opportunity, all smart manufacturers do so to a competitor's products; all intelligent nations do so to the military products of other nations whenever

The Boeing Model 717 (55-3118) prototype for the U.S. Air Force's KC-135A Stratotanker is in the foreground; a 707 prototype turns away in the background.

A Strategic Air Command EC-135 airborne command post from Ellsworth Air Force Base, South Dakota, is one of the variants of the KC-135 that still serve in the U.S. Air Force.

This photo of the Boeing Model 367-80, or Dash 80, prototype clearly shows its debt to the B-47 and B-52 series, with its sweptback wings and pylon-mounted underwing engine pods.

THE 707 PHENOMENON

Boeing's jetliner studies started in 1950 when it scouted the possibility of grafting Mach 0.8 aerodynamics to the fuselage of its Model 367, which the Air Force was buying as its piston-engine C-97 transport and KC-97 aerial tanker. The Air Force needed a jet-powered tanker that could operate at a B-47 bomber's cruising altitude of 40,000 feet. A heavily laden KC-97 could rarely climb above 25,000 feet, forcing B-47s to descend for in-flight refueling; thousands of tons of fuel, costing millions of dollars, were being expended annually by B-47s climbing back to their cruising altitudes.

A "jetified" C-97 would have produced a quick-and-dirty jet tanker and transport, but Boeing knew such an airplane would have no long-term future and that Boeing's engineers could do much better. In 1952 Boeing secretly initiated work on a tanker-transport for the Air Force and a demonstrator for the airlines. To conceal its development from competitors, this airplane was called the 367-80, indicating that it was the eightieth variant of its Model 367, the Air Force C-97. Within Boeing it was known as the Dash 80.

The Dash 80's design, construction, and subsequent operations were not funded by the Air Force, and no airline contributed to its development. This airplane was Boeing's own multimillion-dollar speculative investment.

A 190,000-pound airplane, the Dash 80 flew on July 15, 1954, inaugurating three years of vigorous testing. In 1955 the Air Force ordered 29 greatly upgraded, 297,000-pound tanker-transport variants of the Dash 80. This was Boeing's Model 717, which the Air Force designated its KC-135A Stratotanker. Eventually, the Air Force bought over 600 KC-135s and its various special offspring such as EC-135s, RC-135s, C-135s, and so on.

However good a flying machine it was, the ultimate success of the Boeing 707 was in the increase in diameter of its "tube," or fuselage, by a few inches. Whatever diameter tube an airliner design starts with, it will be the same years later when that airplane goes out of production. The redesign of its fuselage cross section is tantamount to redesigning the entire airplane. A fuselage may be "stretched," that is, lengthened, but once an airliner is in production, its diameter is never widened.

The Dash 80 design had a fuselage diameter of 132 inches, while the KC-135 was 144 inches wide. In an airliner this was enough for 2 + 3 seating, but the airlines wanted space for 3 + 3 seating.

Meanwhile, Douglas came on the scene with its prospective DC-8. Unlike Boeing, Douglas was not locked into a frightfully expensive flying prototype and costly tooling. The DC-8 was a "paper airplane"; with only the flick of an eraser Douglas could promise the airlines anything, and the DC-8 promised a cabin cross section of 146 inches. Fortunately, the 707 was not yet locked into tooling, and Boeing chose to go "two better" and redesigned the 707's fuselage again, now in terms of a 148-inch cross section. This meant losing commonality with the KC-135's fuselage, the necessity of a second production line, and much higher production costs.

The difference of two inches distributed among six seats may sound ridiculous, but where it paid off was in the width of the aisle between the 3 + 3 seating. The willingness to make this change also sent a signal to the airlines that Boeing was deadly serious about the 707 and not simply trying to squeeze an airliner out of its tanker-transport production. As it turned out, Douglas sold 556 DC-8s before the airplane went out of production in 1972, whereas Boeing sold more than 900 of its 707s to the airlines.

Operationally, the 707's 148 inches have stretched across a quarter of a century and will certainly stretch a long way into the twenty-first century. Although most passengers are oblivious to it, when they are travelling in a Boeing 707, 720, 727, 737, or 757, they are all seated in a 148-inch fuselage.

The unusual commonality of tubing among these Boeing airliners inspired an apocryphal story that might be called "The Great Fuselage Machine of Seattle," meaning that Boeing has a machine that turns out one continuous fuselage and production personnel simply slice off however many feet they need for any particular airplane.

The first flight of the 707-120, a 257,000-pound airplane, was made on December 20, 1957. Apparently the same but in fact so different that it required its own production line, the 707-320 intercontinental version, 335,000 pounds, flew on February 15, 1959. Although out of production as an airliner, the 707 is still being produced as a tanker-transport for foreign air forces and as the Air Force E-3A, the Airborne Warning and Control System (AWACS) airplane. As of 1989 some 980 variants of the 707 had been produced.

The most enduring aspect of the Boeing 707 is the name it coincidentally gave to a generation of airline equipment and its technology. Whereas the piston-engine airplanes built between 1936 and 1957 are usually known as the DC-3 Generation, the jet airliners built since 1957 are usually categorized as the 707 Generation.

Body Cross Section Evolution

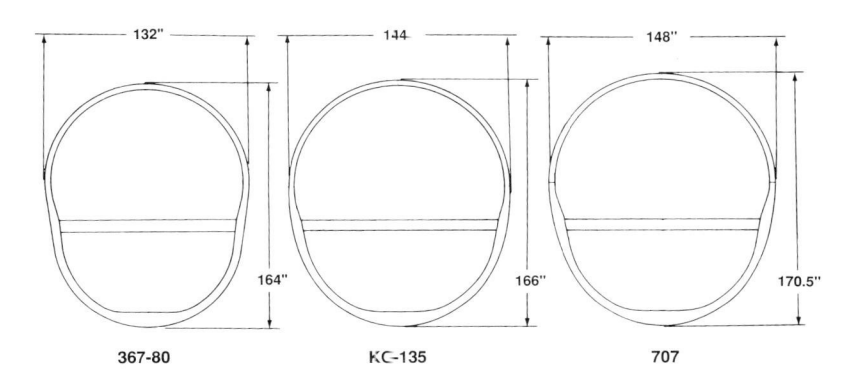

These first two production-model 707s on a Civil Aeronautics Administration certification flight in May 1958 near Mount Ranier, Washington, shortly received full approval for civil airline operations.

After careful testing, the addition of more powerful and fuel-efficient turbofan jet engines greatly improved the performance of the later-model Boeing 707s, such as the 120B and intercontinental 320B/C.

possible. Nor does it necessarily involve "copying"; for that matter, the "copyist" often improves the original product. For the French this 707 provided a valuable learning experience. A great deal of 707 technology was subsequently worked into the French-sponsored Airbus A300, a 300,000-pound airplane that flew in 1972. The Airbus at first appeared to be a loser. However,

BIGGEST AND BEST—THE BOEING 747

By 1959 a typical gas turbine engine produced 16,000 pounds of thrust. This was 13 times the thrust of the unit that powered the Heinkel He 178 of 1939. Engines of 30,000 and 40,000 pounds thrust were already in prospect and the U.S. Air Force started studying the possibility of a million-pound airplane, a transport capable of lifting a payload of at least 250,000 pounds across 8,000 miles.

In December 1964, the Air Force initiated a design competition among Lockheed, Douglas, and Boeing for an airplane to meet these requirements. In August 1965, Lockheed won the contract, the result being the 769,000-pound Lockheed C-5A that flew 34 months later in June 1968. Pan American Airways went to the losers, Douglas and Boeing, seeking an airliner of similar capabilities. At this time Douglas was already in a debilitating corporate confusion that al-

most sent the company into bankruptcy and did result in a merger with McDonnell in 1967. Boeing ran away with the Pan Am business, the result being the Boeing 747, which went on contract in April 1966, and flew 34 months later in February 1969.

Although the 747 was somewhat smaller than the Lockheed C-5A and not burdened by the C-5A's many military complexities, it was nevertheless an initially troubled airplane. This related to an overweight condition relative to available thrust, but was eventually solved. The 747 introduced the "wide body" airplane to the world. Whereas a 707's cabin cross section measures 148 inches, the 747's measures 255 inches. This cross section was determined by the width of two 8-by-8-foot cargo containers because a primary factor in the 747's design was its versatility as a freighter. That the same volume provides many comforts for 350-some passengers is a happy coincidence.

Since introduced to airline service 20 years ago, the 747's design has gone from strength to strength, from the original 747-100 model of 710,000 pounds with seats for some 350 persons, to 1988's 747-400 of nearly 900,000 pounds, with seats for over 400 passengers. The Boeing 747 has become the *Mauretania*, *Queen Mary*, and *Normandie* of the airways; the essentials of its design may still be in production in the year 2018, half a century after its first flight.

This cross-section comparison chart shows why the 747 was called a "wide-body" commercial air transport.

Airlines introduced the initial 747-100 series in 1970.

The Boeing 747-400 on a test flight.

PHOTOGRAPHY CREDITS